CW00820482

Buncefield

Hertfordshire Fire and Rescue Service's
Review of the Fire Response

London: TSO

200365767

Published by TSO (The Stationery Office) and available from:

Online

www.tsoshop.co.uk

Mail,Telephone, Fax & E-mail

TSO

PO Box 29, Norwich, NR3 1GN

Telephone orders/General enquiries: 0870 600 5522

Fax orders: 0870 600 5533

E-mail: customer.services@tso.co.uk

Textphone 0870 240 3701

TSO Shops

123 Kingsway, London,WC2B 6PQ

020 7242 6393 Fax 020 7242 6394

16 Arthur Street, Belfast BT1 4GD

028 9023 8451 Fax 028 9023 5401

71 Lothian Road, Edinburgh EH3 9AZ

0870 606 5566 Fax 0870 606 5588

TSO@Blackwell and other Accredited Agents

First published 2006

ISBN 978 0 11 703716 8

ISBN 0 11 703716 8

Contents

Foreword
by Roy Wilsher, Chief Fire Officer

There are a few dates throughout a firefighter's career that will live for ever in personal and organisational memories. **Sunday 11 December 2005** is one such date. The peace of that early winter's morning was shattered by an initial massive blast closely followed by smaller but still significant explosions. The resulting fire was one of the largest of its kind in peacetime Europe. It presented a significant challenge for everyone involved, not only on a personal level but as a national logistical challenge never before faced by the UK Fire Service. All under the spotlight of national and international media.

Hertfordshire Fire and Rescue Service arrived within minutes and the officer in charge had declared a major incident by 0610. The first firefighters to arrive were met by a scene of utter devastation spread over an immense area. They were presented with a vast and perilous task which saw the involvement of Hertfordshire Fire and Rescue for 26 days. For numerous businesses, people and the community of Hemel Hempstead, the recovery continues. The explosion wrecked homes and businesses in local areas and an excellent partnership approach to recovery continues. Fortunately there were no fatalities and an incredibly low number of casualties. During the working week such an explosion could have had devastating consequences.

Throughout the emergency response, Hertfordshire Fire and Rescue Service personnel showed tremendous commitment, professionalism and skill. Individuals drew on their experience, returning repeatedly to the scene over a number of days to bring the fire under control and later to monitor and maintain the foam blankets.

An unprecedented level of response and support was received from other Fire and Rescue Services, Industry Firefighters and numerous experts who supported Hertfordshire. Government sponsored National Resilience planning was also invaluable, especially the high volume pumps. I am extremely grateful to everyone for their assistance and recognise the value of the equipment and expertise they brought to the response.

We are fortunate in Hertfordshire that our local resilience forum, Hertfordshire Resilience, has been in operation for a number of years. Multi-agency partners were able to pull together in a well practised and coordinated manner. As always, the voluntary sector stepped forward to provide a range of services in support of the fire response, particularly feeding the firefighters. Political support was considerable for the duration of the incident and has continued.

For the Fire and Rescue Service this was a very successful response. The majority of the tanks were extinguished within 36 hours of the foam attacks starting. The main fire was out in 60 hours, fire spread was limited, saving some 36 million litres of fuel, and significant work was undertaken to minimise the environmental impact of the fire and firefighting. Millions of litres of contaminated water were contained on site. Hertfordshire Fire and Rescue Service supported the short term recovery of the site, handing it back to the operators on the 5th January 2006.

There are many positive components of the response to be shared. As always with major incidents there are also additional lessons to be considered with the benefit of hindsight. We hope that this report will enable national and international learning to develop from our experience. I am exceptionally proud of the response of Hertfordshire Fire and Rescue Service and the response of the UK Fire Service. I was informed with the words 'Guvnor, Buncefield's alight' – this report details our response.

Roy Wilsher
Chief Fire Officer
Hertfordshire Fire & Rescue Service

1 Executive Summary

1.1 Outline of the incident and fire response

1.1.1 Early on Sunday 11th December 2005 a massive explosion followed by several other explosions occurred at the Buncefield Oil Storage Depot in Hemel Hempstead, Hertfordshire.

1.1.2 The resulting fire engulfed 20 tanks across seven bunds, later spread to two more tanks, and created a massive smoke plume that rose to several thousand feet and moved towards the southeast.

1.1.3 221 x 999 calls were received, involving seven Fire and Rescue Services' Control rooms across the southeast of England.

1.1.4 Approaching the scene of the incident, the crews declared a Major Incident. Multi-agency command structures were set up to respond and the FRSs Interim National Coordination Centre was activated.

1.1.5 The first fire service activity concentrated on search and rescue. Sectors were defined and systematically searched. Close liaison with the police and companies enabled effective prioritisation.

1.1.6 Initial fire containment commenced at lunchtime on Sunday with water curtains set up to protect uninvolved tanks. Some small targeted foam attacks were made that evening on two tank fires.

1.1.7 Planning and marshalling of resources took place overnight in preparation for a four phased, aggressive foam attack on two fronts. Key difficulties in accessing sufficient foam concentrate and water supplies were overcome.

1.1.8 The first main foam attack commenced at 08:12 on Monday 12th December. HFRS was supported by specialist appliances and crews from industry as well as national FRS equipment and personnel from 31 Fire and Rescue Services.

1.1.9 The majority of the tank fires were extinguished by Tuesday 13th December. The remaining tanks were extinguished on the morning of Wednesday 14th. Localised re-ignitions occurred and bund fires flared until Saturday 17th December.

1.1.10 Water containment and environmental protection were high on the agenda throughout. Recycling was undertaken to minimise the quantity of water used.

1.1.11 Foam blanket maintenance and vapour monitoring continued until 5th January 2006. A site recovery team was formed on Monday 12th December and worked in partnership to begin removing fire water and fuel from the site on Saturday 17th December.

1.1.12 HFRS left the site on 31st December, returning to monitor and apply foam every six hours until 5th January 2006 when the site was formally handed over to the site operators.

1.2 Significant statistics

- 22 Tanks and 7 bunds involved in fire
- 221 x 999 calls to 7 different Fire and Rescue Services
- 31 Fire and Rescue Services supported Hertfordshire
- Four industry fire brigades supported Hertfordshire
- 15 High Volume Pumps used
- Approximately 36 million litres of fuel saved
- 786,000 litres foam concentrate used (+100,000 litres returned)
- 53 million litres of "clean water" applied to fire
- 15 million litres of water recycled and reapplied to fire
- 10 million litres of water moved on site to protect the environment
- 38 km of hose used
- Incident covered area approx 1.5 km by 1 km
- 51 buildings searched
- 1/2 mile radius evacuated (0.8km)
- Window breakage at 2km with further minor damage as far away as 18.6 km
- HFRS supplied 86% of the 642 fire appliances (over duration of incident) and over 90% of the total fire personnel.
- 66 special appliances deployed (over duration of incident)
- First national mobilisation of Fire and Rescue Services by National Coordination Centre

1.3 Summary of report

1.3.1 The fire at Buncefield was unprecedented. The response was very successful; within four days of the explosion all main fires had been extinguished.

1.3.2 This report reviews the fire response drawing out lessons of local, national and international significance. Many learning points come from successful practice at this incident; as always there are areas that could be improved.

Hertfordshire Fire and Rescue Service | Working to Protect. Acting to Save

6

1.4 Recommendations

1.4.1 A series of recommendations as follows:

Chapter 5 Incident Command

1. Hertfordshire Resilience should implement a system for taking forward recommendations from multi-agency exercises and incidents. [5.2.9]

2. Systems and protocols to enable national deployment and extended working of fire resources need to be implemented and tested between FRSNCC and others. All potential responders should adhere to accepted protocols and not mobilise until properly ordered to do so. [5.2.14] [8.3.2] [10.5.10]

3. All local authority FRSs must work to the current edition of the Fire Service Manual on incident command. Other fire responders should be aware of the incident command system and be able to integrate their working practices in order to ensure a safe system of work. [5.2.20]

4. Structured inner cordon procedures must be implemented and maintained at major incidents. [5.3.11] [11.12]

5. A national system needs to be established to maintain an accurate record of all fire responders at the scene that will enable a rapid head count if required. [5.3.11] [9.4.3]

6. Local Resilience forums should develop a single coordinated centre for the acquisition and distribution of all generic resources for all agencies during major incidents. [5.3.23]

7. HFRS should develop and introduce an efficient and effective recording system for all levels of command. It should provide easy access to the decision log and be supported by appropriate technology and training. [5.3.28]

8. Consideration should be given to providing advance warning of redeployments for an extended period to all crews but particularly retained units. [5.4.21]

Chapter 6 Fireground and Functional Sectors

9. A national procedure for the reception, logging and key control of vehicles at incidents involving multiple fire responders should be developed. [6.4.4] [8.4.6]

10. Each fire main pump house and emergency water supply should be positioned and/or constructed such that they cannot be affected by foreseeable incidents. Sufficient hard standing should be provided for the maximum number of mobile pumps that might be expected.

Off site water supplies and their access should be taken into consideration during the pre-planning phase for forseeable incidents at facilities of this type. [6.6.5]

11. Early consideration needs to be given to the type, quantity and duration of deployment of national resources. [6.6.5] [9.8.3]

12. A team of HVP national operational and tactical advisers should be trained and equipped to be deployed anywhere in the U.K. Consideration should also be given to extending this to all National ND resources [6.6.5]

13. Local and national assessments of the likelihood of further incidents should be undertaken prior to the release of FRS resources under national mutual aid. [6.7.5]

14. National standards for the return of New Dimension assets post incident need to be set by the New Dimension team and agreed by all FRSs. [6.9.6]

Chapter 7 Appliances, Equipment and Uniform

15. The New Dimension programme needs to consider the provision and supply of large capacity hose ramps. [7.5.3]

16. Consideration needs to be given to the standardisation of foam couplings or the provision of adaptors between industry and local authority FRSs. [7.8.4]

17. All equipment should be clearly labelled with fuel type, quantities, restart procedures etc. [7.11.2]

18. Earpieces for radios should be introduced to enable communication while wearing a helmet. [7.12.3] [11.7]

19. For incidents requiring national deployment a strategic holding area with adequate facilities should be established. Vehicles should be mobilised from there to the RVP close to the incident and then committed to forward deployment. [7.14.1]

20. New Dimension resources should be identified by FRSs name in addition to the national fleet numbering system. [7.14.2]

21. Modern technology should be used to facilitate briefings, communication and documentary recording. [7.16.5] [8.2.14]

Chapter 8 Control Rooms

22. Future upgrades to Command and Control systems should provide the flexibility required to be able to mix and match crews and appliances. [8.2.9]

Chapter 9 Communications

23. Due to the day and time of this incident, there were no overload problems on the mobile telephone network. A more robust communications system needs to be developed particularly among senior officers. [9.2.9]

24. Sufficient consideration should be given to possible panel members at public meetings, i.e. consider the likely reaction of the public to certain organisations. [9.7.2]

Hertfordshire Fire and Rescue Service | Working to Protect. Acting to Save

8

25.   FRSs should establish mutual aid arrangements with industry fire brigades. [9.8.4]

Chapter 10 Welfare

26.   The provision of toilet, washing facilities and rest areas must be a component in multi-agency response plans. [10.3.4]

27.   Consideration should be given to a national system of incident command support teams that could be deployed during a catastrophic or protracted incident. [10.5.2]

28. A national system should be developed to enable hot debriefs to take place, issues to be recorded and any urgent issues raised to be resolved. [10.6.3]

29.   Consideration should be given to improving the provision of access to information for families of firefighters and on and off-duty members of staff during major incidents. [10.7.3]

Chapter 11 Health and Safety

30. Personnel with operational experience should be appointed at major incidents in order to provide appropriate health and safety advice to the incident commander. [11.10]

List of figures

Hertfordshire Fire and Rescue Service | Working to Protect. Acting to Save

10

2 Introduction

2.1 Buncefield explosions and fire

2.1.1 The fire involved 22 tanks at the Buncefield Oil Storage Depot in Hemel Hempstead, Hertfordshire. It occurred early in the morning on Sunday 11th December, following the explosion of a large vapour cloud and several smaller explosions. An aggressive foam attack on two fronts was used to extinguish the fire. All main tank fires were extinguished within three days of commencing the main foam attack. The overall fire response lasted 26 days.

2.1.2 Hertfordshire Fire and Rescue Service (HFRS) provided 550 of the 642 fire appliance moves to the incident, and over 300 officer attendances. They were supported by 31 other Local Authority Fire and Rescue Services, four industry fire brigades and numerous specialists.

2.1.3 The explosion and resulting fire impacted on hundreds of businesses and necessitated the evacuation of all premises within a half mile radius of the depot. There were no fatalities and the M1 and M10 motorways were both closed at various times during the incident. The smoke plume spread across the southeast of England, over to mainland Europe and was easily visible in satellite photography.

2.2 Scope and structure of this report

2.2.1 The scope of this report is restricted to the fire response. It sets out a chronological record and reviews the fire response. It presents learning points of local, national and international significance, which are drawn from the wide ranging good practice at the incident and from areas that could be improved.

2.2.2 The methodology section sets out the process involved in gathering the data to produce this report.

2.2.3 The chronological account presented in the incident section sets out the key components of the fire response from early on Sunday 11th December 2005 to Thursday 5th January 2006.

2.2.4 Individual sections then consider the learning points from the incident using specific examples. These parts of the report are broken into sections to facilitate ease of reference.

2.2.5 Actual informative messages sent during the incident to HFRS Control in Stevenage are included in capitals at intervals in the text to illustrate the points being made.

2.2.6 Lessons already being implemented by various organisations are noted, the recommendations are set out and conclusions are drawn.

2.2.7 The remainder of this introductory section sets out some background information on HFRS, the Buncefield site and the preparedness for a major incident of this nature.

2.3   Hertfordshire Fire and Rescue Service

2.3.1   Hertfordshire Fire and Rescue Service is a department of Hertfordshire County Council. It covers the local authority area of approximately 600 square miles and serves a population of just over 1.04 million.

2.3.2   At the time of the incident HFRS had 32 fire stations, crewed by a variety of systems (figure 1). The service had 43 fire appliances and a number of specialist vehicles.

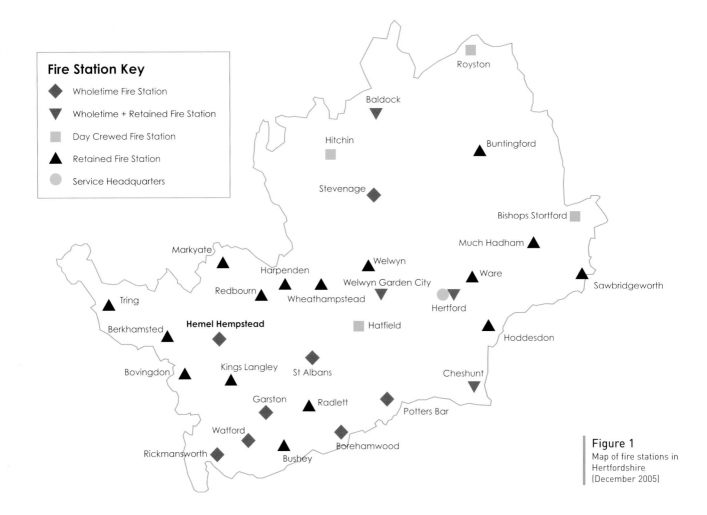

Figure 1
Map of fire stations in Hertfordshire
(December 2005)

2.3.3   HFRS employs 988 personnel (including support staff). This figure includes 45 flexible duty officers and five Principal Officers. In the financial year 2005/06 HFRS responded to 12,933 incidents.

Hertfordshire Fire and Rescue Service | Working to Protect. Acting to Save

12

2.4   Buncefield Oil Storage Depot

2.4.1   The Buncefield Oil Storage Depot occupies a site of approximately 50 hectares to the east of Hemel Hempstead. To the west of the depot is the Maylands Avenue industrial area and to the east are agricultural land and the M1 motorway.

2.4.2   The companies which operate at the site are British Pipeline Agency (BPA), BP Oil UK Ltd and Hertfordshire Oil Storage Ltd (HOSL).

2.4.3 All fuel arrives at the site by pipeline and is transported onwards by either pipeline or road tanker. There are on average 400 tanker movements per day.

2.4.4   The HOSL terminal is split between HOSL East and HOSL West,

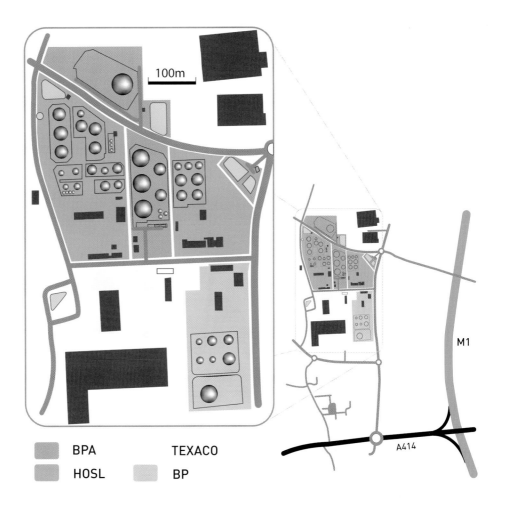

Figure 2
Map of Buncefield oil storage depot

physically separated by the BPA terminal.

2.4.5   The average number of personnel on the Buncefield site during normal operation is approximately 50 during the day and 25 at night.

3 Methodology

3.1 Review Team

3.1.1 Hertfordshire Fire and Rescue Service set up the Buncefield Review in order to better understand and assess what happened in response to the Buncefield incident from a fire service perspective. A full investigation into the cause of this incident is being undertaken jointly by the Health and Safety Executive (HSE) and the Environment Agency (EA) as part of the Major Accident Investigation Board.

3.1.2 The aims of the review were to:

- Gather the information available to produce a chronological record of the fire response;
- Examine the fire response and ensure all the learning points with local, national and international significance were captured.

3.1.3 A team was formed to conduct the review, reporting to Deputy Chief Fire Officer Mark Yates. The service received assistance from the Office of the Deputy Prime Minister (now Department of Communities and Local Government (DCLG)) and Hertfordshire County Council's Emergency Planning Team in forming the team as follows:

3.1.4 Senior Divisional Officer Gordon MacMillan on secondment from the Office of the Deputy Prime Minister led the team, supported by Emma Message and Easher Hill both on secondment from Hertfordshire County Council's Emergency Planning Team.

3.1.5 The team collated all available material in order to produce this review. In particular, it has considered:

- Pre-planning and pre-training;
- The fire response by Hertfordshire Fire and Rescue Service;
- The response by other fire providers and supporting organisations.

3.2 Collation of information

3.2.1 All materials generated by Hertfordshire Fire and Rescue Service during the course of the incident have been collated. This includes logs produced at fire silver and bronze, multi-agency silver and multi-agency gold commands, and at HFRS Control.

3.2.2 All information has been electronically catalogued.

3.2.3 All flexible-duty officers were required to verify their incident attendance data and provide information on the activities undertaken during each shift associated with the incident. This enabled a clearer picture of the Incident Command System (ICS) to be developed.

3.3 Official debriefs

3.3.1 A series of internal debriefs were held to verify the sequence of events and the decision making process behind them. These debriefs focussed on HFRS personnel and included external fire agencies where appropriate, in particular for the specialist functional debriefs for foam and water.

3.3.2 In addition every crew, watch and station were asked to conduct their own debriefs and feed into five district debriefs. HFRS officers were also requested to complete the HFRS debrief form to catalogue their experiences of the incident.

3.4 National survey

3.4.1 A national survey of fire services was conducted to confirm what resources were deployed to the Buncefield incident. Data was supplied by individual service control rooms and collated by the Fire and Rescue Service National Coordination Centre (FRSNCC) in West Yorkshire.

3.5 External debriefs

3.5.1 Incident information and debrief reports were requested from all other Fire and Rescue Services that attended. Meetings were held with Essex County Fire Service, London Fire Brigade, BPA and others to gain further information.

3.5.2 Requests were also sent to organisations which had provided a significant contribution to the incident, for example foam suppliers and site operators.

3.6 Timelines

3.6.1 A significant proportion of the data received related to particular time periods of the incident. Timelines have been built from different sources and a combined incident chronology developed from the key data.

3.7 Data review day

3.7.1 A review day was held to categorise all qualitative data received. Representatives from different roles, ranks and districts within HFRS, plus representatives from other services, New Dimension and industry were involved. The HSE also observed this process.

3.7.2 Each point was categorised according to the headings in the HFRS debrief form to produce some quantitative information on the feedback received. This data has been used to give a sense of scale to the various issues raised in this report.

3.7.3 Three caveats should be noted when interpreting this data. First, the HFRS debrief process has been designed for watch and station use for normal sized incidents. It does not necessarily transpose well to being used in the multi-agency, multi-brigade, multi-company environment.

Hertfordshire Fire and Rescue Service | Working to Protect. Acting to Save

16

3.7.4 Secondly, during debriefs there is a tendency for comments of a negative nature to come to the fore in large quantities, whereas positive comments tend to only be mentioned if they are significant. This is generally accepted, but it can distort the quantitative data to some extent.

3.7.5 Finally, very few officers made contemporaneous notes for the incident. This has been an issue for data gathering, as not only have memories become blurred, but the relative importance of specific issues has been re-gauged as a result of numerous informal discussions and the passage of time.

3.8 Multi-Agency Issues

3.8.1 The scale of this incident tested multi-agency systems beyond normal business. The multi-agency issues are not covered in detail in this report, but referenced where a multi-agency decision had a key impact on the fire response.

3.9 Major Accident Investigation board

3.9.1 The HFRS review team adopted a completely open book policy with the Major Accident Investigation Board (MAIB). Members of the MIAB attended numerous debriefs. They were also supplied with a range of information as requested. The MAIB assisted the HFRS review where legislation permitted. Sharing of information has reduced the total number of debriefs and interviews required and has aided accuracy and consistency.

4 The Incident

4.1 Overview

4.1.1 This section presents the chronology of the fire response to the incident from early on Sunday 11th December 2005 to Thursday 5th January 2006.

4.2 Explosion

4.2.1 On Sunday 11th December 2005 a massive vapour cloud explosion occurred at the Buncefield Oil Storage Depot in Hemel Hempstead, Hertfordshire.

4.2.2 Before the explosions, a vapour cloud had spread in all directions including drifting westwards towards the adjacent industrial estate, crossing a large car park and appearing on CCTV images as a low level white mist (Figure 3)

Figure 3
Map of extent of
the vapour cloud
(Denoted by red line).
Data supplied by
the HSE

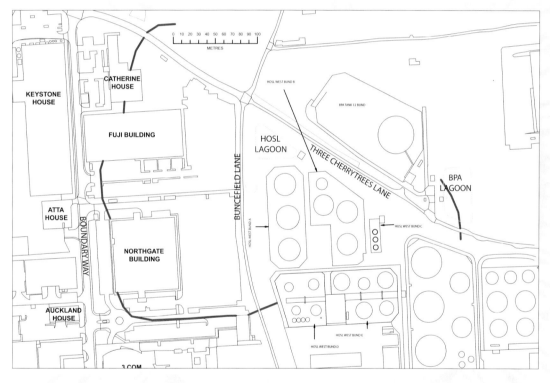

Tanker drivers in the Hertfordshire Oil Storage Ltd (HOSL) West site observed this mist and raised the alarm just before the first explosions occurred.

Mist cloud taken
from CCTV

Before build up of mist cloud

Mist cloud

Mist cloud taken from CCTV

Before build up of mist cloud

Mist cloud

4.2.3 The most significant blast measured 2.4 on the Richter scale 29km away and the sound wave recordings (figure 4) indicate that it could be heard 200km away.

Figure 4
Geological survey data

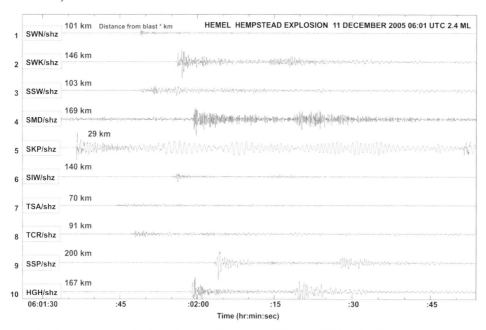

The explosions caused significant damage (figure 5) including:

- Catastrophic structural damage to or rupturing of 19 tanks and numerous buildings on site;

- Structural damage to all but four of the other tanks on the site;

- Blocked access to two of the three emergency water reservoirs;

- Destruction of the fire main pump houses on site;

- Severe structural building damage to properties within 1km of the depot;

- Broken windows, displaced internal and external walls and collapsed ceilings in industrial, residential and educational buildings up to 2km from the depot;

- Minor damage and displacement of items, such as loft hatches, at 18.6km.

Hertfordshire Fire and Rescue Service | Working to Protect. Acting to Save

20

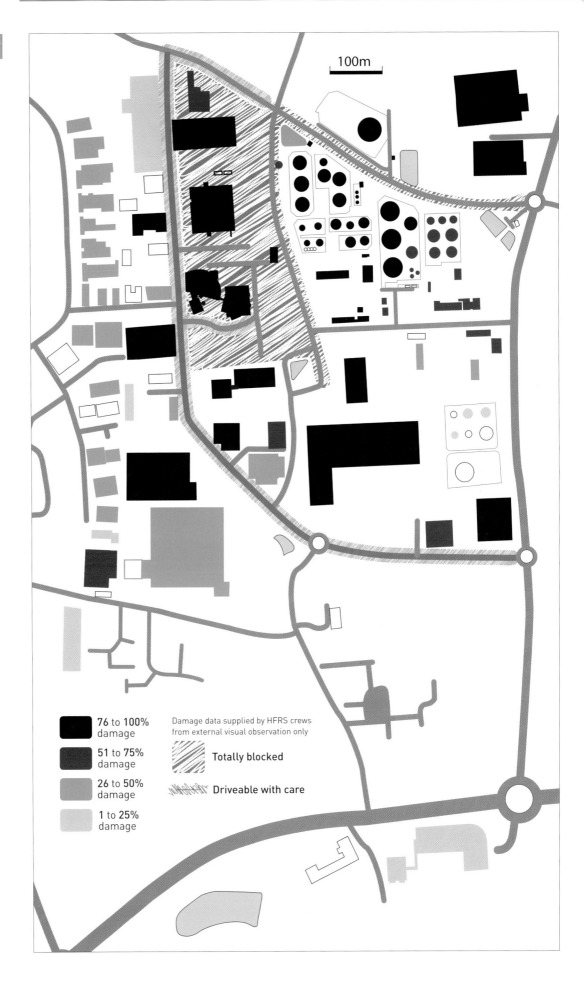

Figure 5
Map of blast damage

100m

76 to **100%** damage

51 to **75%** damage

26 to **50%** damage

1 to **25%** damage

Damage data supplied by HFRS crews from external visual observation only

Totally blocked

Driveable with care

4.2.4 As a result of the explosions:

- Fire engulfed 20 tanks across seven bunds (one of which was a rim fire on tank 4) (figure 6)

- A significant smoke plume was generated that rose sharply and moved towards the southeast;

- Northgate building caught fire;

- Numerous car fires and other small fires occurred.

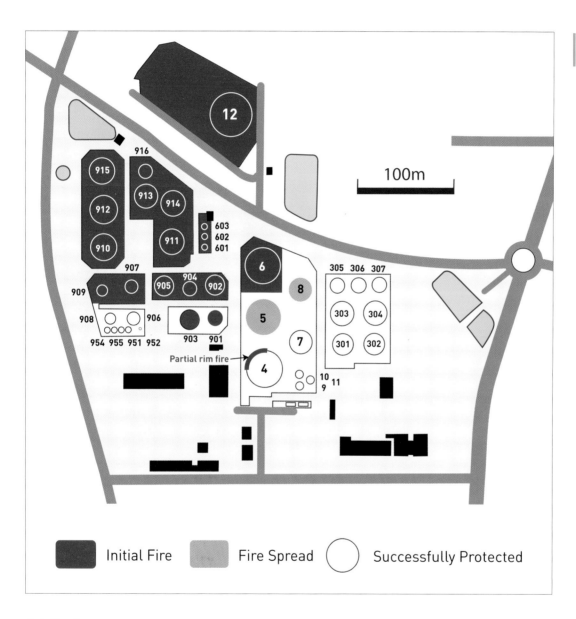

Figure 6
Map of initial tanks on fire

Initial Fire   Fire Spread   Successfully Protected

4.2.5 Bedfordshire & Hertfordshire Ambulance and Paramedic Service (BHAPS) conveyed 9 patients to hospital. Following the incident health sector records show a total of 36 self presenters at Hemel Hempstead Hospital.

4.2.6 There were 370 businesses on and around the Maylands Avenue industrial estate affected by the blast damage with many more experiencing the knock-on effect. Several residential properties close to the site were also severely damaged.

Hertfordshire Fire and Rescue Service | Working to Protect. Acting to Save

22

Metropolitan Police
helicopter image
taken at 06:55
showing bunds fully
involved in fire (left)

Chiltern Air Support
helicopter image
taken at around 9am
(Right)

06:55:56 24H   SU 11/DEC/05

4.2.7 Many people in Hertfordshire and beyond were woken by the blast with the furthest 999 call being taken by West Midlands Fire Service some 151 km away. Crews at Hemel Hempstead fire station 4.3 km from the depot, heard the blast and mobilised at the same time as Hertfordshire Fire and Rescue Service (HFRS) Control began receiving emergency calls. The first explosion was determined to have been at "06:01:31.45 UTC with a robust uncertainty of 0.5sec" (British Geological Survey Report) and preceded a number of lesser explosions. The explosions were so severe that one driver deemed it to be safer hiding under his articulated petrol tanker, which was parked at the loading gantry, rather than immediately evacuating.

4.3 Initial response

4.3.1 During the period immediately after the explosions, FRSs across the southeast of England received 221 x 999 calls relating to the blast. HFRS Control handled 56 of these calls, plus 54 calls from Automatic Fire Alarms. Emergency calls cited a wide range of locations and numerous causes (figure 7). This required the four Hertfordshire control room staff on duty to filter the information received and make decisions on the number of separate incidents that had occurred.

Figure 7
Map of 999 call
distribution

4.3.2 The first two crews from Hemel Hempstead fire station approached the area at 06:06 via Maylands Avenue. On route, they saw the plume and exploding fireballs and "made pumps 8". As they got nearer, they began to assess the level of devastation, the extent

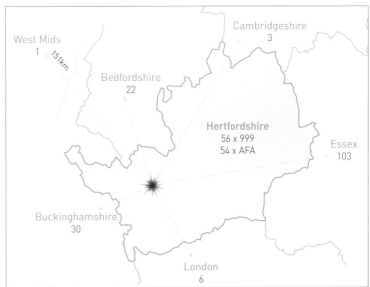

West Mids
1   151km

Cambridgeshire
3

Bedfordshire
22

Hertfordshire
56 x 999
54 x AFA

Essex
103

Buckinghamshire
30

London
6

of the fire and the associated smoke plume. HFRS Control logs the assistance message at 06:10:44 from the Officer in Charge of the first attendance "This is declared a Major Incident". On the strength of the information being received into the control room the Officer in Charge in HFRS Control increased the initial response to 12 appliances.

4.3.3 The two appliances from Hemel Hempstead continued their approach from the south using Green Lane. Accessing the depot via the main gate, the crews encountered several workers from the depot all of whom were suffering from either blast injuries or shock.

4.3.4 Site personnel followed laid down procedures and vacated the site, albeit with some alacrity! Employees who remained at Buncefield activated the emergency plans. They provided a map of the site and some valuable information to aid firefighting. Initially, there were six unaccounted personnel, all thought to be in the vicinity of the HOSL West loading gantry.

> 11/12/2005
> 06:18 Informative   MAJOR FIRE IN TANK FARM OF OIL TERMINAL.
> APPROX 6 PEOPLE MISSING NUMEROUS CASUALTIES REPORTED.
> EFFORTS BEING MADE TO CONTACT SITE MANAGEMENT.
> REDEPLOYMENT OF FIREFIGHTING SERVICE ACCESS FOR ON
> COMING APPLIANCES VIA M1 MOTORWAY BREAKSPEAR WAY
> BUNCEFIELD LANE. TACTICAL MODE DELTA

4.3.5 The Officer in Charge held the Hemel Hempstead appliances at the main entrance and proceeded on foot with one firefighter to carry out a dynamic assessment of the scene. They began to search the areas of greatest danger for survivors. As they were searching the HOSL site control room there was another large explosion, which caused debris to fall on them. Having completed a rapid sweep of this building and concluded that the identified risk outweighed any potential benefits, they exited to direct the crews. As they left the building, there was another severe explosion which nearly knocked them over.

4.3.6 Appliances approaching the scene had to weave through the explosion debris and avoid the many roadway inspection covers which had been displaced. From as early as 06:30, they encountered significant numbers of the public travelling towards the fire to view the spectacle. This caused some access problems. Hertfordshire Constabulary were already setting up road blocks and cordons. In particular they were requested to close Three Cherry Trees Lane running to the north of the main Buncefield site.

4.3.7 The initial rendezvous point RVP, (figure 8) was set up at 06:24 directly outside the main gates of the site. This was rapidly moved back to the roundabout junction of Green Lane with Boundary Way (RVP2) at 06:43. A nearby police motorway post was also used as an RVP for a short period. By this time the crews had ascertained that there were about 40 private cars on site and that they could not account for all persons. Following a further dynamic assessment it was determined that there was a slim possibility that survivors could be located around the tanker loading gantry area. Two officers undertook a search of this area which was found to be clear. No areas nearer the exploding tanks were searched at this time.

Hertfordshire Fire and Rescue Service | Working to Protect. Acting to Save

24

Figure 8
Map with RVP's

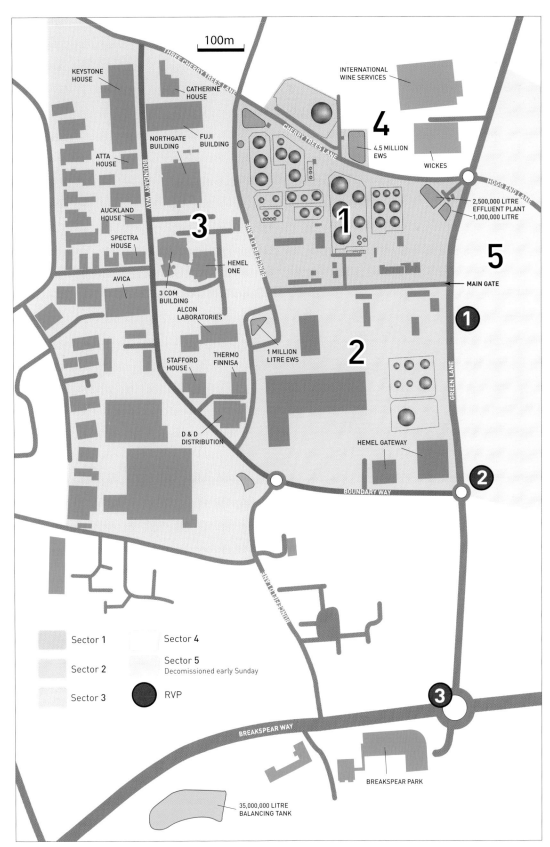

Figure 8
Map with RVP's

4.3.8 At the same time other crews proceeded to the warehouses to the north of the site at Hogg End Lane. These appeared to be alight, but were in fact just reflecting the flames from the terminal site.

4.3.9 During the initial searches, both on and off site, crews observed tanks which they considered to be on the brink of collapse. There were further significant explosions, after which crews noted an increased smell of aviation fuel.

4.3.10 By 06:45, the HFRS Control Unit was in operation at the police motorway post close to the M1 junction 8. It was re-positioned at the roundabout junction of Green Lane and Breakspear Way at 07:19. The RVP (RVP3) had been moved further back to the vicinity of Breakspear Park on Breakspear Way for safety and to enable marshalling.

11/12/2005
06:47 Informative MIN OF 6 TANKS WELL ALIGHT - AT LEAST TWO MORE DAMAGED BY EXPLOSION - TM DELTA - AT LEAST SIX PERSONS UNACCOUNTED FOR

4.3.11 Initial assessments on the ground of the scale of the incident were communicated to HFRS Control at 06:47 informing of "at least six tanks well alight". Crews could not gain 360 degree access or vision of the site mainly due to routes being blocked by debris. (By 08:00 the extent of involvement was revised to include 20 of the tanks at the site.) The Metropolitan Police helicopter was in attendance from approximately 06:46 enabling further assessments to be made from the air, but the Fire Incident Commander could not access the downloaded images at that time. An air exclusion zone was put in around the area. An officer from HFRS was taken by helicopter to review the scene shortly after 09:00 and report back to the command support team on the full extent of the incident.

4.3.12 By 06:58 a half mile radius evacuation zone had been ordered by the Fire and Rescue Service and standard public safety messages were being issued to the areas beyond this zone, i.e. to go in, stay in, tune in (with windows and doors closed). The whole of the M10 motorway was closed. The M1 motorway was closed from the M25 Junction to Junction 9. It reopened on the Sunday evening. Junction 8, the Hemel Hempstead turnoff, remained closed until Friday 16th.

4.3.13 Crews were deployed to the only accessible on-site water supply identified in the site fire plan, the Million Litre emergency water supply (EWS). From their position, members of the crew observed and reported the Northgate building on fire. HFRS Control deployed two appliances and an

Crews at the Million Litre EWS

Aerial Ladder Platform (ALP) to the Northgate building at 07:33. The access along Boundary Way was problematic due to the amount of debris and dead or injured wildlife on the road with crews having to weave through or stop to clear the route.

Hertfordshire Fire and Rescue Service | Working to Protect. Acting to Save

26

4.3.14 By this time the Deputy Chief Fire Officer (DCFO) and an Assistant Chief Officer (ACO) had arrived at the scene, been briefed by the initial officers and crews, undertaken a reconnoitre by car and were developing action plans. At 07:47 the DCFO took command of the incident with the ACO taking up the role of Command Support with executive responsibility.

4.4   Command systems

4.4.1 A major incident was declared by several organisations within Hertfordshire Resilience on Sunday morning. Hertfordshire Constabulary activated multi-agency gold and silver commands to manage the incident. Figure 9 shows the location of each command.

Figure 9
Location of
Commands

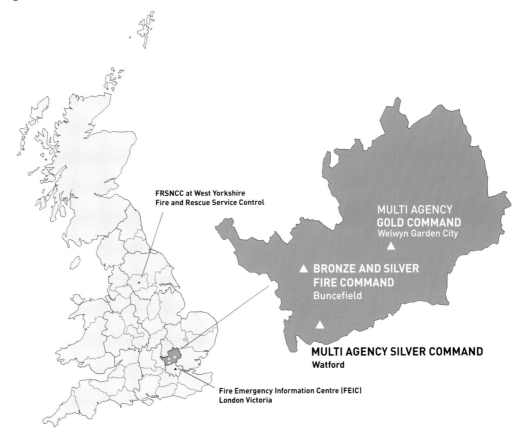

4.4.2 Following agreed pre-planning arrangements multi-agency gold was set up at police headquarters in Welwyn Garden City, chaired by Hertfordshire Constabulary. Other key organisations were quickly represented. Strategic fire command was provided by HFRS Chief Fire Officer (CFO). He attended the multi-agency gold command meeting at 09:00 to advise and consult other agencies, and provide media interviews. Support was provided at this location by other HFRS officers.

4.4.3. The Incident Commander requested that Fire Gold identify and mobilise specialist firefighting advice.

4.4.4 Multi-agency silver command was initially located in relative proximity to the scene at the Leverstock Green Village Hall. An HFRS ACO was deployed there to act as Silver Command liaison. Shortly after, multi-agency silver was moved to Watford police station to enable better access to communication systems. HFRS sent an ACO to Watford at about 09:30, again supported by officers as they became available.

4.4.5 HFRS Control continued to operate from Stevenage throughout the incident. Other FRSs were involved in receiving 999 calls and making contact with significant other organisations on behalf of HFRS. For example, following liaison with HFRS, Buckinghamshire Control contacted the main foam suppliers, Angus Fire, at 07:06 to alert them of the incident.

4.4.6 The Fire and Rescue Service National Coordination Centre (FRSNCC) based in West Yorkshire Fire and Rescue Service was requested to activate at 07:50. HFRS invited the duty officer from HM Fire Service Inspectorate to attend multi-agency gold command to liaise between the Fire Emergency Information Centre (FEIC) and FRSNCC. The FEIC acted as the gold command for the FRSNCC and provided professional advice to central government. Many other organisations set up various levels of command at their home locations, including foam suppliers, industry firefighters and other local authority FRSs.

4.5 Search sectors

4.5.1 A review of the draft site fire-plan confirmed that it was insufficient for the scale of the incident. The degree of destruction to the HOSL control room and fixed firefighting apparatus in the initial explosions and the number of tanks involved meant that a new dynamic plan was required.

> 11/12/2005
> 08:02 Informative   APPROX 20 TANKS BELIEVED INVOLVED IN FIRE -
> BLAST DAMAGE OVER A LARGE AREA - SEARCH IN PROGRESS OF
> AREAS AND BUILDINGS - NO FIREFIGHTING ACTION TM DELTA

4.5.2 Five topographical sectors (figure 8) were initially established to devolve responsibility for particular operations. Sector 5 was quickly decommissioned as it was largely agricultural land. The main focus in all sectors was search and rescue. As it was early on Sunday morning, all indications were that very few people were in the vicinity. However, there were some unconfirmed reports of unaccounted people. By Sunday night the police casualty bureau had received over 11,000 calls. There was no loss of life at this incident and the longest hospital stay was two days.

4.5.3 Sector 1 at this stage was the Buncefield site itself. Further searches were made throughout the site. At the same time, the availability of fixed firefighting installations and on-site water supplies were reviewed. Areas for early firefighting and cooling to prevent fire spread were identified. In addition, isolating the on-site utilities and silencing the site alarm system were prioritised.

Hertfordshire Fire and Rescue Service | Working to Protect. Acting to Save

28

Figure10
Damaged buildings
Images show face
of building nearest
to Buncefield site

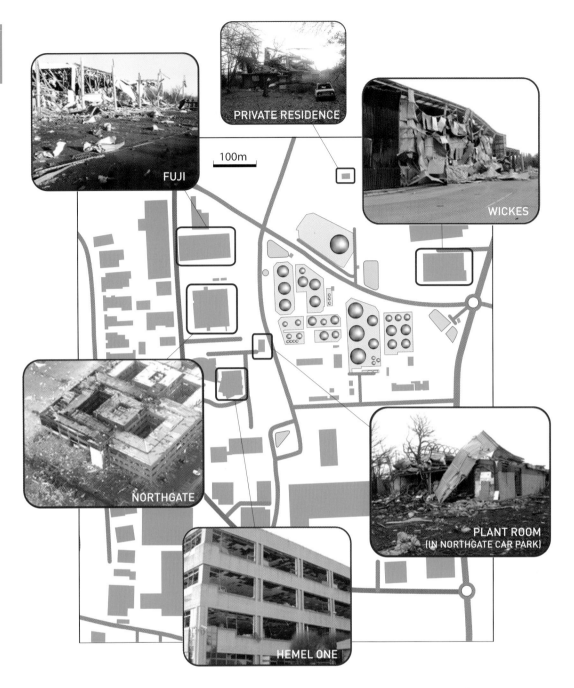

4.5.4   The tactical decision made at this time was that the "fire" was a contained event; given the logistical planning required to achieve controlled extinguishment, only boundary cooling was planned at this stage. This was to prevent the fire spreading to unaffected tanks.

4.5.5   Sector 3 was a large firefighting and search sector to the west of the Buncefield depot in the Maylands Avenue industrial area. Buildings were prioritised and systematically searched on the basis of survivability. Personnel were not committed into the most structurally damaged buildings unless there was a clear indication that people were inside. Systematic searching confirmed there were no further casualties (figures 10, 11, 12).

4.5.6   An ALP was deployed to the Northgate building to assist in assessing the fire. The assessment was carried out using thermal imaging cameras from the platform and ground level observations. At this time there was only a small fire of about 4m by 4m. Limited firefighting was then undertaken. One 45mm hose line was lashed in place.

Figure 11
Four faces of the
Northgate building

4.5.7   Initial crews searched, to the best of their ability, the buildings nearest the epicentre of the explosion. They discovered a large number of private cars and evidence that people had been injured. Crews were then reorganised to undertake a more systematic search of all properties. Very few personnel were committed to the buildings due to concerns over the buildings' structural integrity. The Sector Commander and Incident Commander discussed the requirement for specialist rescue crews from either United Kingdom Fire Service Search and Rescue Teams (UKFSSART) or the New Dimension program Urban Search and Rescue units (USAR). Based on all the information, they agreed at this time not to request specialist rescue teams.

4.5.8   While the systematic search was ongoing the smouldering fire in the Northgate building flared up. It was later attended by six appliances and an ALP.

Northgate building fire
with Buncefield in the
background

4.5.9   Firefighters in sector 3 identified a strong smell of gas and called in specialists to isolate the supply. The effect of radiated heat from the Buncefield site was reviewed before closing this sector. Of particular concern was an exposed nitrogen tank within the car park of the 3 Com building.

Hertfordshire Fire and Rescue Service | Working to Protect. Acting to Save

30

Figure 12
Damage Fuji
Building

4.5.10 Sector 4 was to the north of Buncefield. A further search of the warehouses at Hogg End Lane did not reveal any casualties. Crews were withdrawn from these buildings as there was evidence of structural damage and confirmation was received from the security firm that all personnel were accounted for. This sector was then closed down with the crews being redeployed to the Million Litre EWS.

Bonded warehouse
at Hogg End Lane
from the air

4.5.11 Sector 2 was similar to sector 4. Some of the properties in this sector were new and had not yet been occupied. It was quickly established that there were no operationally significant issues to be addressed in this area.

4.6   Initial fire containment

4.6.1   It became evident, from the search operations and the police, that there was a very low probability of finding further casualties. Resources were re-focussed on the Buncefield site. The tactical mode remained at Delta, defensive, until midday on Sunday 11th December 2005.

11/12/2005 11:12 Informative AS PREVIOUS-STEADY PROGRESS IN
SEARCHING AREAS SURROUNDING BOUNDARY WAY, MAYLANDS
AVE AND THREE CHERRY TREES LANE-FIRES UNDER CONTROL IN
THESE ARFAS-COOLING JETS BEING LAID OUT AROUND
PERIMETER OF TANK FARM-CALCULATIONS FOR FOAM ATTACK IN
PROGRESS-TM DELTA

4.6.2 Preparations were made to establish cooling jets to prevent the fire
spreading to unaffected tanks. As the response began to focus on the fire
itself, the depot was re-sectorised into two (figure 13). Significant quantities of
foam had already been identified and mobilised; although nothing like the
amount that would be needed according even to initial calculations.

4.6.3 The first cooling jets were applied shortly after midday using water
sourced from the Million Litre EWS. Five appliance pumps delivered at over
600,000 litres per hour to areas around the site including:

- Four lines of 70mm to water curtains to protect the road tankers at
  HOSL West loading gantry;

- Four lines of 70mm to water curtains to protect the unaffected tanks
  in HOSL bund D;

- Six lines of 70mm to provide a water curtain between the involved BPA
  site and the as yet uninvolved HOSL East site.

Cooling jets
in operation

4.6.4 Following consultation with industry experts, who were on site to
assess the stability of a number of tanks, withdrawals from the site were
ordered. On Sunday 11th there were two partial withdrawals at 13:48 and the
second at 15:00 when the majority of personnel were withdrawn to a safe
distance leaving limited firefighting operations in progress.

Hertfordshire Fire and Rescue Service | Working to Protect. Acting to Save

32

Figure 13
Fire containment
sectors also showing
hose lines Sunday
daytime

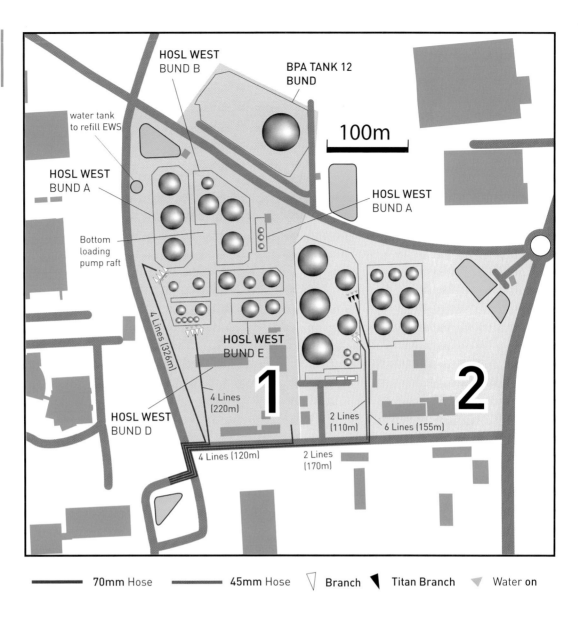

HOSL WEST
BUND B

BPA TANK 12
BUND

100m

water tank
to refill EWS

HOSL WEST
BUND A

HOSL WEST
BUND A

Bottom
loading
pump raft

4 Lines (326m)

HOSL WEST
BUND E

1

2

4 Lines
(220m)

HOSL WEST
BUND D

2 Lines
(110m)

6 Lines (155m)

4 Lines (120m)

2 Lines
(170m)

——— **70mm** Hose   ——— **45mm** Hose   ▽ **Branch**   ◤ **Titan Branch**   ▽ Water **on**

4.6.5 Interestingly initial advice received from industry sources was that some tanks were empty. On further investigation the term empty had differing meaning for industry and firefighters. For those in industry "empty" tanks contain up to 1 million litres of product that is undrawable. In firefighters' terms, 1 million litres does not equal empty!

> 11/12/2005
> 16:34 Key LONDON SENDING 3RD FOAM APPLIANCE
>
> 11/12/2005
> 20:35 Key 3 STAFFORDSHIRE FRS PUMPS AND STAFFORDSHIRE
> FRS HVP IN ATTENDANCE

4.6.6 Throughout the afternoon and evening, other FRSs, national resources and industry firefighting specialists were arriving at the scene (Figure 14). This included personnel and equipment, particularly HVPs, lighting and foam. At intervals HFRS Control tried to ascertain numbers of vehicles and personnel as few external crews had booked in with them.

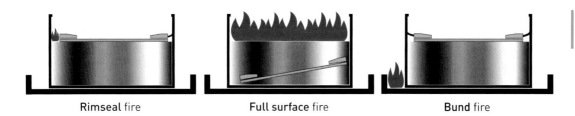

Figure 14
National resources arriving at the incident

11/12/2005
17:32 Informative AS PREVIOUS INFORMATIVE FOAM EQUIPMENT BEING LAID OUT TO TACKLE PERIPHERAL AREAS OF TANK AND BUND FIRES MAJOR WATER SUPPLY LOCATED READY FOR HIGH VOLUME PUMPS SILVER COMMAND INFORMED BULK FOAM SUPPLY INCREASED TO 170,000 LITRES COOLING JETS STILL IN PLACE FIRST STAGE FOAM ATTACK PLANNED FOR 19.00 HRS TM TANGO

4.6.7 The first foam attack commenced at just after 17:00. It tackled the rim seal fire on BPA tank 8 to prevent or at least delay this tank becoming involved and possibly affecting the next tank farm. Initially this was attempted using the semi-fixed foam pourers but aborted over concerns that the lid would tip over.

Figure 15
Tank fire scenarios

Rimseal fire   **Full surface** fire   **Bund** fire

Early foam attacks

Hertfordshire Fire and Rescue Service | Working to Protect. Acting to Save

34

11/12/2005
20:54 Informative AS PREVIOUS INFORMATIVE STEADY PROGRESS
BEING MADE WITH COOLING, COOLING JETS REPOSITIONED 1 TANK
RIM SEAL FOAMED STILL AWAITING FULL FOAM ARRIVAL MAIN
WATER SUPPLY BEING ESTABLISHED USING HIGH VOLUME PUMPS
MAJOR LIGHTING BEING POSITIONED TACTICAL FOAM ATTACK
PLAN BEING ORGANISED ENVIRONMENT AGENCY AND THAMES
WATER ADVISED ON POSSIBLE FOAM RUN OFF TM TANGO

Foam attack in the darkness

4.6.8 The second foam attack started at 21:07. It focussed on and successfully extinguished HOSL tank 909 within five minutes. This involved crews working together to supply six lines of 70mm hose and 4,000 litres of foam concentrate to the site provided Titan foam monitor. In order to achieve this, significant work had to be undertaken to reduce the number of cooling jets and reposition the hose.

4.6.9 During Sunday, there was a pressure fed fire in bund E that was causing intense heat radiation towards the tankers in the loading area. Repeated calls by company representatives were necessary before the supply was turned off.

4.7 Planning Phase

Figure 16
Map of four foam attack phases by bund

4.7.1 The Plan – Following a request from the Incident Commander mid- morning on Sunday 11th, the CFO, in consultation with multi-agency gold, took the strategic decision to extinguish the fire, rather than allow it to burn out. This was relayed to the DCFO at the incident ground.

4.7.2 A comprehensive action plan was not formed until many options had been assessed and reviewed. The initial plan at 17:40 was for an attack on two fronts. The main limiting factor here was the foam/ water/ hose

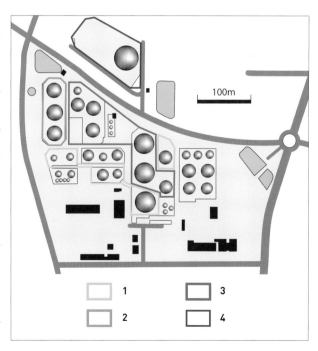

infrastructure and logistics required. At this time it was calculated that a 60 minute attack would be sufficient. However, different functions used different factors in calculating resources to allow for contingencies (figure 16). It was calculated to require 2,250,000 litres of water at a rate of 25,000 litres per minute and 150,000 litres of foam concentrate. These figures were continually revised.

4.7.3 At 17:30 FRSNCC was requested to contact FRSs and the Fire Service College to request the mobilisation of 14 High Volume Pumps and support crews. These HVPs were to be at the incident by 22:00.

4.7.4 The Fire Gold Commander had to consider numerous strategic issues about the timing of the foam attack. Multi-agency gold was advised that by mid-afternoon on Monday 12th the plume would be over northern France. The consequences of firefighting had to be balanced against the implications of allowing the fire to burn. Main areas for consideration included:

- Land and air pollution and the difficulty in acquiring definitive data on which to base decisions;

- Disruption to the roadway infrastructure;

- Disruption to the residential and business community;

- Public image of HFRS not tackling this fire.

Plume of smoke over the M1 motorway

4.7.5 A key decision was centred around the timing of the main foam attack. A night time attack was considered better for the public, who would mostly be inside and therefore less affected by the cooling and subsequent settling smoke plume. However, even with good lighting this needed to be balanced against the additional hazard of a night attack for fire crews.

Hertfordshire Fire and Rescue Service | Working to Protect. Acting to Save

36

4.7.6 The final major Firefighting Plan was received at Gold Command from the DCFO and included specific detail of firefighting water containment:

Two prong foam attack.

1) Total foam tender down side of 908, 909, 910. Water supplied from EWS (HFRS pumps). 40 mins of attack self contained. Then 20k foam bowsers. 7,500l/minute.

2) Six gun (TOTAL) towards 903, 901. Water from HVP. Foam concentrate from foam tankers 40k + then 20k bowsers. 23,000l/minute.

- Max total water 1.92m litres per hour. This is at maximun capacity continually - unlikely but the planning assumption.

- All areas bunded as follows | 906 - 909 | 910,912,915 | 911,914, 913, 916 | 901-905 | avtur 4-8 | tank 12   301-307 |

- All bunds sound, capable of containing at least 2+ hours of application

- Tank 12 left to last - difficult access + assessment due to location.

- *RUN-OFF*
  Water treatment complex in NE corner pumped empty water - into bund 301-307. Capacity 2.5m litres - 1 hour 20 minutes of run-off.

- Anticipate little or no run-off due to bunding. If run off noticed 1 hour period of catchment.

- Knock off of application via sector commanders (x2) radio contact and immediate knock off of HVP.

- Spotters to be placed with sole job of viewing run-off.

- If water treatment complex is getting full HVP set in to pump to BP tanks due south of water treatment complex - capacity 5m litres plus.

- Respiratory Protection
  TOTAL staff have EDBA (60 minutes). Consideration being given to HFRS personnel. Predicted plume will fall over top of immediate site.

Prior to implementation, the above plan was reviewed due to concerns raised by the Environment Agency relating to run off and the ever diminishing water supply.

4.7.7 Meetings - at the request of the DCFO a group was formed to plan the logistical requirements for the main foam attack. It was chaired by a HFRS Divisional Officer and included fire officers from industrial brigades, other local authority FRSs and other specialists with industry expertise.

4.7.8 From mid-afternoon on Sunday 11th December, they based themselves at Breakspear Park House, calculating the likely water, foam and associated equipment requirements. The attack was originally scheduled to commence at midnight.

4.7.9 In calculating the quantities for foam concentrate, the planning group made the following assumptions:

- Fire size approximately 100m x 100m;

- Foam concentrate application rate 8 lpm/m^2 (based on published data on application rates);

- Foam concentrate application at 3%.

4.7.10 For an hour long attack this was rounded up to 150,000 litres of foam concentrate. This was doubled to 300,000 litres to allow a significant margin for error and allow foam for blanket maintenance.

4.7.11 In terms of water, the calculations were based on a Six Gun requiring a supply of 25,000 litres per minute and further water needed for cooling jets. It was agreed that at least 40,000 litres per minute would be required at 8 bar. This equated to nine HVPs with a further three available to provide spare capacity.

4.7.12 Functional commanders were assigned the task of establishing the appropriate supply chains for foam and water to implement the plan. The foam attack planning team held a first review of the DCFO`s plan at midnight on Sunday 11th. Sufficient resources were not yet in place to commence the main attack and would not be for some hours, but it was agreed to continue with the four phased attack plan.

4.7.13 At approximately 02:00 all sector commanders were briefed. They agreed to start the main attack once the hose was laid, as sufficient foam stocks were now on the scene or in transit.

4.7.14 A further meeting of key players was held at 03:00 to review progress and to reconfirm the plan. As no personnel had any direct experience of dealing with an incident of this duration and complexity, the timescales which were originally agreed proved to be unrealistic. Several times during the Sunday night and the early hours of Monday notification was given that a foam attack would commence at a specific time, which then passed. The main foam attack actually commenced on Monday at approximately 08:30. Additional meetings were held in multi-agency gold to confirm that the above plan was acceptable to all agencies.

Hertfordshire Fire and Rescue Service | Working to Protect. Acting to Save

38

4.7.15 Water source - the on-site water sources were recognised as being insufficient. By Sunday lunchtime, the search for a suitable alternative supply had begun. At about 15:30 a New Dimension High Volume Pump expert arrived at multi-agency silver command. Of the four water supplies considered the Grand Union Canal was the most notable water course in the general area of Hemel Hempstead. At 16:00 ACO Operations, from multi-agency silver command, contacted British Waterways for authorisation on extraction from the Grand Union Canal at a rate of 25,000 litres per minute.

4.7.16 After some hours three main concerns were raised in relation to using the canal as the primary water source:

- Collapse of the Grand Union Canal under the required rate of water extraction;

- Sufficient HVPs available in the country to provide the required pumping capacity over the required distance and head;

- HV hose through Hemel Hempstead would generate significant disruption, especially given closure of M1 junctions.

4.7.17 At 17:40 the idea of using balancing tanks was initially raised. There were a number of balancing tanks in the area, but they were known to be seasonal, so a site visit to each potential tank was required to establish current volume of water.

4.7.18 At 22:00 a fireground calculation of the volume of water in the Breakspear Way Balancing Tank (Balancing Tank) was carried out and estimated to be 35 million litres. This was calculated by pacing the length and breadth. The depth was plumbed using a weighted line from the mobilised boat crew.

4.7.19 35 million litres was considered sufficient to provide water for the planned duration of the major foam attack. This Balancing Tank was confirmed as the primary water source.

4.7.20 Access to the Balancing Tank was initially planned from the south via the residential road, Wellbury Terrace (Figure 17). As with other potential water supplies this route was considered but discounted due to overcoming head, difficulty in accessing the supply and the disruption to residents.

4.7.21 From 02:00, significant work was undertaken to gain access to the Balancing Tank from the north and enable the deployment of HVPs and their hose. A considerable number of fire appliances and other vehicles/equipment needed clearing to one side of the carriageway of Breakspear Way to enable the hose to be laid. Access to the water's edge involved the removal of a section of fence, clearance of vegetation, including significant tree branches and the laying of hardcore (type 1) as a temporary road. Insufficient hard core was available to extend the road to the water, so a crane was employed at 03:00 to move the HVPs into position.

0   50   100
metres

823 metres

Wellbury Terrace

Figure 17
Map of Wellbury
Terrace and the
initial proposed
route of HV hose.

Work at the
Balancing tank
to deploy HVP's.

4.7.22 By 06:00 all HVPs were in position at the Balancing Tank. Hose laying from the Balancing Tank to the fireground was fully in place by 07:00. An individual line was charged first to test the relay, then all others were charged.

4.7.23 Closer to the fireground, supply systems for foam and water were established between 04:00 and approximately 07:00 on Monday 12th December. The preparations comprised:

- Hose supplying cooling jets being made up and transferred to west of loading gantry in preparation for foam attack;

- Making up of excess hose and identification of remaining lines;

- Establishing communications between different components of the firefighting operation;

Hertfordshire Fire and Rescue Service | Working to Protect. Acting to Save

40

- Establishing water relay with three pumps near loading gantry to supply 6 lines 70mm to Total foam tanker in preparation for the attack from the northwest - each line was approximately 12 lengths long.

12/12/2005
06:03 Informative AS PREVIOUS INFORMATIVE - ALL HIGH VOLUME PUMPS IN POSITION - HOSE LINES BEING LAID IN PREPARATION FOR FOAM ATTACK - RESERVOIR DRAINED TO RECEIVE POTENTIAL RUN OFF - BA DUMP BEING SET UP - FOAM CONCENTRATE AND EQUIPMENT BEING POSITIONED - TM OSCAR

fireground distribution of HV hose from the air

4.7.24 Whilst undertaking these preparations, the fire spread situation was reviewed and cooling jets were continually monitored, maintained and repositioned to prevent further tanks becoming involved in the incident. For example, cooling was applied in the vicinity of tank 5 at about midnight, as tank 901 was glowing red.

4.7.25 Water containment - Issues were raised by the Environment Agency (EA) personnel at the scene on Sunday. Dealing with the contents of ruptured tanks and fire water/foam run off was a vital component of planning for the foam attack and all cooling operations. This planning was undertaken in conjunction with the EA prior to the eventual plan being agreed. (Figure 18)

Figure 18
Section diagram of Buncefield site topography. Image supplied by HSE.

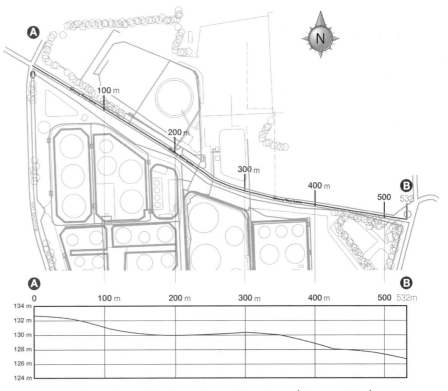

Ground profile along Cherry Tree Lane (West to East)

4.7.26 Foam marshalling - Initially foam supplies were gathered from FRSs adjacent to Hertfordshire. Foam was offered from a large number of sources. The first bulk foam was mobilised from Buckinghamshire FRSs at 07:22 on Sunday 11th. Arriving stocks and equipment were stockpiled on the M10 motorway from then onwards.

4.7.27 At 13:06 the FRSNCC were tasked by FEIC with conducting a survey of available and appropriately sized bulk foam supplies and lighting. They surveyed all FRSs. In turn the FRSs surveyed any significant military or industrial sites that could release foam or appropriate equipment. Confirmation of the national availability of all foam stocks was received by HFRS Control at 18:29.

Foam Marshalling

4.7.28 It rapidly became clear that large quantities of foam would be required. A designated Foam Officer contacted all the organisations identified by HFRS Control to order foam stocks. Capturing the estimated time of arrival of the foam stocks was seen as crucial by the Foam Officer. This officer ordered over 150,000 litres of foam, the figure suggested in early assessments by experts in attendance at the incident.

4.7.29 The majority of this foam had arrived at the fireground by 23:00, with approximately 177,000 litres available prior to the main attack commencing.

4.7.30 The requirement for foam in large containers (no smaller than 1000 litres) was recognised by the Incident Commander. The importance of this specification was understood throughout the supply chain. Despite this significant quantities of foam were supplied in 25 litre containers and proved useless given the rate at which the large specialist foam equipment used concentrate.

4.7.31 fireground personnel used their initiative to enable foam to be collected from different containers and then delivered to foam equipment and branches.

Foam lorry

4.7.32 Due to the fact that the HV hose had closed off one of the available lanes on Green Lane, a manual "traffic light" system had to be created and operated by HFRS. The bulk foam lorries were marshalled in order of anticipated use with both quantity and type of foam considered. At the same time it was crucial for safety to maintain decent egress routes from the site.

Hertfordshire Fire and Rescue Service | Working to Protect. Acting to Save

42

4.7.33 On site the vehicles were marshalled at the forward holding area situated in the HOSL West compound, near the tanker loading gantry, and directed from there for use.

Figure 19
Sequence of tank
extinguishment

4.8 Main foam attack

4.8.1 All equipment and resources were in place to commence the attack by breakfast time on Monday 12th December. The plan for the attack, particularly the water containment element, was reconfirmed through multi-agency gold command prior to commencement.

12/12/2005
08:33 Informative AS PREVIOUS
INFORMATIVE - FINISH FOAM NOW
BEING APPLIED TO FIRE - TM
OSCAR

4.8.2 All multi-agency commands were informed of the commencement of the main foam attack. The attack was commanded at all levels by HFRS officers who were strongly supported by industry firefighters, other FRSs and various specialists. The supporting infrastructure comprised 90% of the work and was supplied by HFRS crews and New Dimension resources from a further 31 FRSs. Foam was applied using the specialist equipment and expertise of firefighters from industry and other Local Authority FRSs.

4.8.3 The wind had changed direction so the smoke plume was moving in a south south-westerly direction and was more turbulent. This altered the plan a little, requiring the crews approaching the fire from the west to move further to the north of the site. Their focus also shifted from tank 915 to 916, as tank 915 had collapsed. This required the hose lines to be extended and was the first of many minor refinements to the initial plan (Figure 19).

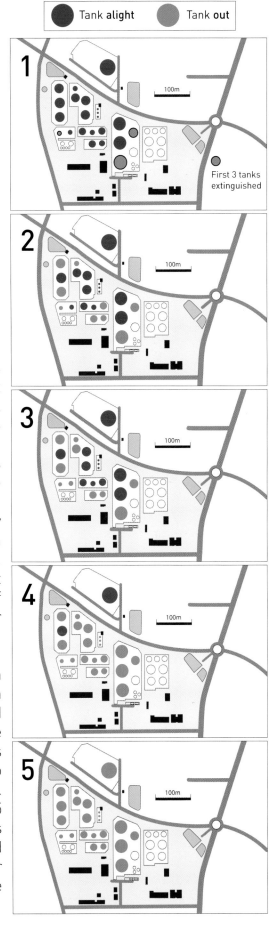

4.8.4 The other foam attack commenced in the southeast corner, focussing on tanks 901 and 903 and commenced as planned.

4.8.5 HVP crews pumped water for approximately one hour. Then the foam making equipment was repositioned and foam application recommenced for a further 90 minutes. The foam blanket had to be reapplied to extinguished areas approximately every 15 minutes to prevent re-ignition. By 11:56 nine tanks had been extinguished. Maintaining the foam application continued using a mixture of aspirated handheld branches and non aspirated pourers.

Main foam attack

4.8.6 As the foam was applied and the effect of the thermal currents diminished the smoke plume became much more unstable. This resulted in worsening visual and respiratory working conditions. Some pumping crews wore breathing apparatus for comfort with other crews being rotated every 10 minutes.

4.8.7 On Monday at 13.18 a running fuel fire, caused by HOSL West bund E slightly overfilling and "slopping over", forced crews to withdraw to 20m away. An additional five pumps were requested to deal with running fuel fires and a "Make pumps 25" was relayed to HFRS Control. Further risk assessments were undertaken prior to recommencing foam application.

Main foam attack

4.8.8 A significant withdrawal followed at approximately 14:00 requiring crews to be withdrawn to a safe distance from tank 7. This tank was being affected by the fire at tank 5 and was considered liable to rupture. The monitors were left in use during the withdrawal with periodic checking by limited crews under exceptionally tight control.

12/12/2005
14:05 Informative TANK 7 ADVISED MAY RUPTURE ALL CREWS EVACUATED 6 MONITORS LEFT IN USE - T M DELTA.

4.8.9 Crews remained withdrawn for much of the afternoon. Risk assessments and operational planning were aided by the downloaded images from the Chiltern Air Support Unit helicopter at 17:15. Two crews were re-introduced to maintain cooling jets and deal with run off.

Hertfordshire Fire and Rescue Service | Working to Protect. Acting to Save

44

4.8.10 The pipeline manifold area just to the south of the BPA bund was extensively cooled during Monday. Foam concentrate continued to be delivered. By 18:00 over 143,000 litres had been delivered by Angus Fire alone.

4.8.11 HFRS Principal Officers were involved with the multi-agency public and business briefings on Monday and Tuesday evenings. These meetings were to allay fears, address health and safety concerns and generally report on progress.

Damaged hose after running fuel fire

4.8.12 Throughout the evening, cooling jets continued to be applied to un-ignited tanks on the site. Water was being redistributed around the bunds in a continual effort to balance the firefighting and environmental considerations, namely to prevent the contamination of surrounding water courses.

4.8.13 At 22:00 the local electricity company (EDF) notified multi-agency silver command that the substation could be affected by rising water levels. Some crews were withdrawn to a safer distance while a reassessment took place. EDF attended the scene and isolated the substation by 01:00.

4.8.14 Tank 5 had ruptured by the early hours of Tuesday 13th December, raising concerns that Tank 7 and then the HOSL East tank farm could become involved. To prevent this, cooling jets were reapplied to tank 7.

4.8.15 This further commitment of water increased the need to consider sourcing more water and further action to deal with containment. With an application rate of approximately 32,000 litres per minute, a recycling system was put in place to address both issues. Contaminated water from the effluent plant was recycled for use by cooling jets, while clean water was used for the production of foam. Water containment was also addressed through a circulation system, pumping water from the effluent plant works, to the BP bunds using HVPs, then when advice was received that these bunds could lose their containment, back to the effluent plant.

4.8.16 The issue of containment again re-emerged on Tuesday 13th at 04:21 when some water overflowed from the treatment works. Further action was taken emptying the treatment works into the bunded areas on BP site.

13/12/2005
04:08 Informative AS PREVIOUS - COOLING CONTINUING -
DEVELOPING NEXT PHASE OF FOAM ATTACK - ELECTRICITY
CONFIRMED ISOLATED - GOLD INFORMED - TM OSCAR

4.8.17 Cooling continued throughout the morning. A foam attack on the three tanks alight (901, 912 and 12) and the bottom loading pump raft was developed with an initial view to commence at 09:30. At 11:00 firefighters were withdrawn from sector 1 for 20 minutes due to the severity of the fire in HOSL West bund A. It was later, at 13:36 that firefighting action commenced on two of the remaining three tanks alight. Crews tackled tank 901 from the south using the Patriot monitor, while a Six Gun was used on tank 12. Water was supplied using HVPs based at the Balancing Tank, which by this time was being replenished from the town mains supply.

4.8.18 At 16:39 the incident log records "last tank fire extinguished". However, efforts to extinguish all rim and bund fires continued into the evening and next day. Persistent flaring continued within several bunds, especially where the foam blanket degraded for a number of reasons.

13/12/2005
16:39 Informative LAST TANK FIRE EXTINGUISHED - ACTION BEING
TAKEN TO EXTINGUISH RIM FIRE - BUND FIRE REIGNITION
EFFORTS BEING MADE TO REINSTATE FOAM BLANKET - VARIOUS
FOAM BRANCHES IN USE - T M OSCAR

Preparations for
maintenance of
foam blankets

Hertfordshire Fire and Rescue Service | Working to Protect. Acting to Save

46

4.8.19 The pressured flange fire from tank 912 was a particular challenge overnight on the 13th/14th December. Specialist firefighters at the scene considered attempts to isolate the flange unlikely to succeed, so they agreed to allow this fire to burn. An estimated 6 million litres of petroleum spirit initially fed the fire. Following consultation between the Incident Commander and the CFO, the decision was taken to allow this to burn to reduce the amount of product and prevent a vapour cloud forming. This fire was later extinguished.

Tank 912 in flames (left)
Tank 12 in flames (right)

Tank 912

4.8.20 By 05:25 tank 912 was showing signs of collapse so crews were withdrawn from this area. The tank collapsed before 07:00. Elsewhere the foam blanket was continuously maintained using various foam equipment and supplies.

4.8.21 A joint investigation team, led by the police and involving HSE and HFRS, had been formed on Monday 12th. The decision was taken to commence the practical on-site fire investigation on 14th December.

4.8.22 During Wednesday 14th December, there was some melting of the joining compound in the bund walls around tank 12. Fire water run off caused flooding at Hogg End Lane, under the M1 bridge; at 11:20 five pumps were deployed to deal with this. Sand bags were used to contain it.

4.8.23 Further action was taken to reduce potential site run off through the redeployment of high volume pumps during the afternoon.

4.8.24 In the late afternoon, activity focussed on maintaining the foam blanket and making up equipment as it became redundant. The Stop Message was sent by the DCFO on Wednesday 14th December at 19:36:27.

RESIDENTIAL AND COMMERCIAL AREA COMPRISING NUMEROUS
BUILDINGS OF 1,2,3 AND 4 STOREYS. 22 STORAGE TANKS SEVERELY
DAMAGED AND 4 STORAGE TANKS MODERATELY DAMAGED BY FIRE
ALL BUILDINGS IN STORAGE DEPOT AND COMMERCIAL AREA
SEVERELY DAMAGED BY BLAST. VARIOUS LEVELS OF DAMAGE TO
RESIDENTIAL AREAS. MULTIPLE FOAM MAKING EQUIPMENT JETS
HIGH VOLUME AND FIRE SERVICE PUMPS AND ASSOCIATED
EQUIPMENT USED

4.8.25 Maintenance of the foam blanket and making up continued on Thursday
15th December. Foam stocks were replenished every few hours. Foam
supplied by Angus Fire on 14th and 15th December reached over 360,000
litres. HFRS endeavoured to release resources (equipment and personnel)
from other FRSs.

15/12/2005
05:28 Informative AS PER PREVIOUS - AMENDMENT TO SECTOR
COMMANDERS - SECTOR 1 STNO MACDONALD - SECTOR 2 AND 4
STNO STRATFORD - SECTOR 3 ADO PRIEST(BUCKS) - EGRESS NOW
AVAILABLE FOR ALL UNDAMAGED PETROL TANKERS TO BE
COLLECTED BY OPERATORS - TM OSCAR

15/12/2005
10:41 Informative SA FOAM BLANKETS MAINTAINED
RECOVERY OF EQUIPMENT IN PROGRESS EFFORTS BEING MADE TO
RELEASE RESOURCES PROVIDED BY OTHER SERVICES VARIOUS
ITEMS OF EQUIPMENT IN USE TM OSCAR

4.8.26 At 12:30 on Thursday 15th December "FIRE ALL OUT" was declared.

4.8.27 During this period the HFRS's trainee firefighters were given the
opportunity to gain some insight into a major incident by visiting the scene and
assisting in the make up where their level of training permitted.

4.9   Maintaining until 05 January 2006

4.9.1   Following the fire all out message, HFRS maintained a permanent
presence on the site for a further 15 days.

4.9.2   The focus of operations shifted to monitoring, reapplying foam to
maintain bund blankets, environmental protection and considering the
handover of the site in the longer term.

15/12/2005
22:11 Informative 189-FOLLOWING SITE MEETING AT 21.00HRS A
TARGET TIME OF 12.00HRS ON FRIDAY 16TH DEC HAS BEEN
AGREED FOR COMMENCEMENT OF REMOVAL OF CONTAMINATED
RUN OFF FROM INCIDENT-TM OSCAR

4.9.3   On Friday 16th December the foam concentration application rate was
still 2,000 litres per hour. The wind was causing the blankets to break up,
requiring further application. At this time, there were no fires on site and all

Hertfordshire Fire and Rescue Service | Working to Protect. Acting to Save

48

Foam blanket
maintenance

run off was contained. The circulation systems for fire water were still in place.

16/12/2005
17:23 Informative   FOAM APPLICATION CONTINUING TO THE FOAM
TANKS, SUPPRESSION FOAM BEING SUPPLIED TO BUNDS, 4
PUMPS PROVIDING FOAM, 3 PUMPS PROVIDING WATER, EXPLOSIVE
LIMITS BETWEEN 0 AND 0.2. TM OSCAR

Hose make up

4.9.4   During the afternoon of the 16th all equipment was made up and retrieved from Breakspear Way, enabling this road to be re-opened at 20:00. The HFRS Control Unit was relocated to inside the depot, close to the HOSL West loading gantry. Many nationally mobilised resources and adjacent FRSs personnel were released and returned home.

4.9.5   A site recovery group was set up to consider the ongoing site issues. This was chaired by HFRS ACO Operations while HFRS maintained a presence on the site. The membership included the Health and Safety Executive, Environment Agency, site operators and their contractors. Daily meetings were held to agree environmental protection measures, triggers for further firefighting action and procedures and priorities for the removal of product and fire water from the site.

4.9.6 From Thursday 15th December, members of the site recovery group worked to agree a method for removing product with a view to commencing this by 12:00 on the 16th. The first removal actually took place on 17th December at 14:10.

4.9.7 Monitoring systems were set up using gas detection monitors and explosimeters, enabling both gas and liquid sampling. Air samples were taken every 30 minutes at six locations. A series of threshold points for further action were agreed as follows:

- Fluid flashpoint under 50 degrees Celsius;
- Air 25% of lower explosive limit.

On reaching either threshold a site meeting would be convened to agree a response. This monitoring was carried out by HFRS personnel who had been trained by industry representatives.

4.9.8   By Saturday 17th December, the flashpoints being recorded were high, and it was agreed to stop applying foam to the bunds, but leave foam making and other firefighting equipment in situ. The site recovery team agreed that equipment could be gradually made up as areas were deemed no longer at risk.

17/12/2005
10:41 Informative AFTER A SITE MEETING WITH APPROPRIATE REPRESENTATIVES WE HAVE AGREED TO STOP APPLYING FOAM TO BUNDS AND ESTABLISH A PRODUCT SAMPLING AND AIR MONITORING SYSTEM. TM DELTA

4.9.9   Just a few hours after halting foam application, a fire in HOSL bund C reignited. This followed the passage of a low flying light aircraft and helicopter over the site. Foam was reapplied, extinguishing the fire in less than 30 minutes.

4.9.10 An aerial survey of the site that afternoon prompted further foam to be applied to the four tanks in bund E. High volume pumps were restarted to deal with the run off.

4.9.11 The last major consignment of 60,000 litres of foam concentrate was delivered by Angus Fire on Saturday 17th.

4.9.12 Freezing temperatures overnight caused additional challenges with hose lines becoming frozen. Several lengths of hose needed to be replaced and anti-freeze measures were put in place. The freeze-thaw action may have further affected the integrity of the bund walls. At 20:12 concern was raised that the bund wall of tank 12 might loose its integrity.

Run off adjacent to site

4.9.13 The focus on Sunday 18th December was containment of run off in the area of Hogg End Lane area. Personnel in this area took the precaution of wearing respirators or full breathing apparatus. In addition, the pipe work to tank 914 reached the threshold flashpoint so further foam was applied in this area.

Hertfordshire Fire and Rescue Service | Working to Protect. Acting to Save

50

4.9.14 The air exclusion zone was lifted at around midday on Monday 19th December following a further assessment by helicopter. Product removal was gearing up around bund E, the BPA lagoon and adjacent roadway with HFRS required to provide escorts, monitoring and firefighting protection to contractors operating in these areas.

4.9.15 A meeting of the site recovery team resolved to reduce the threshold level for fluids from 50 to 35 degrees Celsius. Foam application equipment was also reconfigured to concentrate cover on the area around bund E and the corner of bund C, nearest to tank 12.

4.9.16 During the night, run off increased in Cherry Tree Lane, accompanied by a significant increase in fumes. Damming and diverting were undertaken using sandbags.

> 18/12/2005
> 22:02 Informative PREVIOUS WATER RUN OFF NOW CONTAINED USING SANDBAGS - AREA CONTINUALLY BEING MONITORED - TM OSCAR

4.8.17 Over the next few days, monitoring continued, with foam application required less and less often. National resources continued to return home in stages. On 24th December the HFRS presence on site was reduced to two pumps day and night. At 16:00 on Christmas Eve, all contractors left the site.

4.9.18 On Christmas Day, the HFRS crews on site reapplied foam to maintain the blanket where the wind was affecting it. They also took precautions against the cold weather, running all engines for 5 minutes and draining, applying frost protection and reconnecting all hose.

> 28/12/2005
> 18:21 Informative 189-STNO NOW OIC-INFORMATIVE-CONTINUING EXPLOSIMETER READINGS AND MAINTAINING WATCHING BRIEF

4.9.19 The last national resources, one HVP and lighting from London Fire Brigade, were released on 28th December.

4.10 Closing of operations and transfer of responsibility

4.10.1 On 30th December, it was agreed with Total and HSE that a permanent HFRS presence would no longer be required. Equipment was left on site and six hourly reapplications of the foam blanket were programmed for Hemel Hempstead and St Albans crews. The Total representative would contact HFRS Control if required and two potential levels of response were agreed:

- In the event of increased petrol smell, two pumps and a flexible-duty officer would be mobilised;

- In the event of a fire, a full pre-determined attendance of eight pumps would be mobilised.

4.10.2 Under these conditions, the permanent site presence ceased at 15:35 on 31st December 2005.

4.10.3 Crews attended Buncefield at six-hourly intervals for the next five days. During each visit they reviewed the situation and the status of the foam blankets, spending up to 90 minutes on site. HFRS passed responsibility for on site risk assessment to the site operators at 16:10 on 5th January 2006 and the incident was closed.

Job done!

Buncefield six months on

Hertfordshire Fire and Rescue Service | Working to Protect. Acting to Save

52

5 Incident Command

5.1 Overview

5.1.1 This section explores the command systems that were established and examines how these operated during the incident.

5.1.2 Away from fireground, command structures were set up in line with recognised multi-agency structures. At the incident scene, HFRS Control Unit and sector commands were set up. Key incident command issues that arose relate to protocols of different commands operating together, identification of key personnel and inner cordon control. Communication played a role in these and other issues and will be noted in this section and analysed in more depth later in this report.

5.2 Structures

Figure 20
Example of
Command Structure

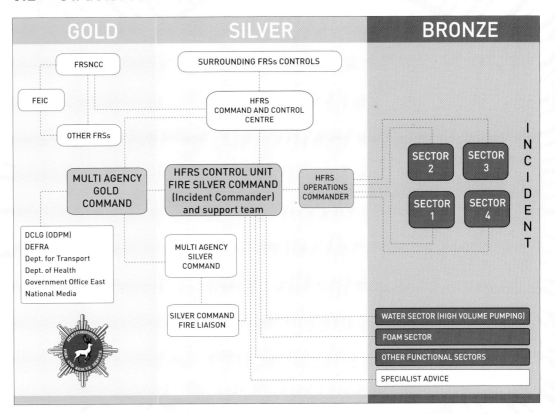

5.2.1 **Multi-agency commands** - The main learning points for this element will be addressed by the multi-agency debrief report. This section is intended to give an initial overview.

5.2.2 Multi-agency command systems were initiated according to long established and well rehearsed procedures set out by Hertfordshire Resilience, formerly Hertfordshire Emergency Services Major Incident Committee (HESMIC). HFRS sent representatives to the pre-designated gold and the initial and subsequent multi-agency silver commands (figure 21). At the time of going to press initial feedback is largely positive on multi-agency cooperation.

5.2.3 The decision was taken to operate both Fire Bronze (Operational) from close to the scene and Fire Silver (Tactical) from the HFRS Control Unit and the facilities available at Breakspear Park House. This is often the approach taken by FRSs during major incidents and was particularly relevant as this was a "fire incident". It enabled close consultation between those operating on the fireground and those making tactical decisions.

5.2.4 The Principal Officer initially deployed to multi-agency silver command did so in a liaison role.

5.2.5 The CFO attended the multi-agency gold command, which was located at Hertfordshire Constabulary HQ. Resilience forum partners from all relevant agencies attended this command (Figure 21).

Figure 21
Hertfordshire
Resilience

Hertfordshire Constabulary
Hertfordshire Fire & Rescue Service
Beds & Herts Ambulance & Paramedic Service
Hertfordshire County Council
The District & Borough Councils of Hertfordshire
Hertfordshire's National Health Services
Voluntary Agencies
Environment Agency
Utility & Transport companies

5.2.6 Both the Gold Commander and Silver Liaison were to be supported by a variety of officers. As they became available HFRS Interagency Liaison Officers (ILOs) were utilised. The ILO system had been recently established within HFRS. The service had identified designated ILOs and commenced training in this role.

5.2.7 HFRS consider that some non-blue light organisations had either devolved limited power to those at the scene or not provided their personnel at the scene with all the relevant information in order to give the best advice. On occasion multi-agency agreements made at silver and bronze were subsequently overturned at a higher level. The speed of response following a request for information or a decision varied greatly from organisation to organisation. In the early dynamic stages of an incident when information is of a variable nature decisions still have to be made - the "best information available decision" has to apply occasionally. It was felt that some organisations arrived at decisions by committee processes rather than by command.

5.2.8 This was a protracted incident and as it progressed all those trained for the ILO role were utilised. Additional personnel not identified or specifically trained also carried out the role. The trained ILOs had additional awareness of

Hertfordshire Fire and Rescue Service | Working to Protect. Acting to Save

54

multi-agency issues and importantly existing personnel contacts. There was no marked difference between ILOs and non-ILOs in terms of their record taking, the structure of which could be improved.

5.2.9   As the incident progressed, there were occasions when there was more than one Principal Officer at the fireground. These officers were carrying out different roles such as hosting VIPs, conducting media interviews or re-familiarising themselves with the incident. Divisional Officers (DO) and even Station Officers (STN O) were in attendance at multi-agency silver and gold. They could contact Principal Officers by telephone. However, this caused some confusion in relation to the incident command system for HFRS personnel, other FRSs and partners. This is acknowledged in the Fire Services Manual:

> "If a fire incident escalates to a 'Gold' level event, it is entirely probable that the fire Incident Commander, who may be a Chief or Assistant Chief Officer, will assume incident command, sending a lower ranking officer to act as liaison at 'Gold'. It can be seen that positions are role, rather than rank, related." (Fire Service Manual, Volume 2, Incident Command, 2002)

Recommendation 1
Hertfordshire Resilience should implement a system for taking forward recommendations from multi-agency exercises and incidents.

5.2.10 Main control (HFRS) & other fire controls (Fire and Rescue Service National Coordination Centre, other FRSs) - HFRS Control and those in adjacent FRSs handled the initial burst of 999 calls and contact between them was rapidly established. Some stacking and automatic re-routing of incoming calls was necessary. Local resources were mobilised to the scene. HFRS Control performed their role as expected and where necessary adapted pre-set protocols to meet the changing demands.

5.2.11   As the scale of the incident became clear, resources were mobilised effectively in line with HFRS's major incident procedure. The FRSNCC was requested to activate at 07:50 on the 11th by the Duty Officer of HM Fire Service Inspectorate.

5.2.12   Given that no personnel in any of the controls or communication hubs had any direct experience or agreed protocols or procedures for working together, the system worked exceptionally well in initially mobilising the required resources to the fireground.

5.2.13   The main issues that arose were:

- Insufficient notification to mobilise for a national incident of a protracted nature;

- Range and quality of national "turnout" information including RVPs, expected duration, welfare arrangements, etc;

- Communication systems issues between all FRSs and FRSNCC;

- Communications systems issues between FRSNCC and FEIC;

- Prolonged and frequent use of mobile phones bypassing communications hubs and controls.

5.2.14 The role of HFRS Control was at times blurred. It was not always clear whether HFRS control was operating as a total resourcing centre, or undertaking the more limited role of a mobilisation and communications hub.

Recommendation 2
Systems and protocols to enable national deployment and extended working of fire resources need to be implemented and tested between FRSNCC and others. All potential responders should adhere to accepted protocols and not mobilise until properly ordered to do so.

5.2.15 **Forward control** - Debriefs strongly support the view that the quality of forward control varied during the incident. The initial set up and organisation of the search sectors during the Sunday morning and early afternoon was in line with expectations at an incident of this nature.

5.2.16   At the incident, the HFRS Control Unit was set up some 950 metres from the main gate to the site. This allowed space for marshalling and the safety of the position enabled medium term tactical planning to be undertaken from there. In line with common practices this was viewed as the Fire Silver, with Sector Commanders operating as Fire Bronze.

HFRS Control unit
(Fire Silver)

5.2.17 At the commencement of the incident two Principal Officers were mobilised to attend. The DCFO took command at 0747 hrs and remained until 1700 hrs on Sunday 11 December. The ACO was in the Control Unit throughout the day and continued when he took over as the Incident Commander from 1700hrs until midnight on the Sunday when the DCFO returned. During the day the ACO was tasked with assisting the Incident Commander and due to the scale of the incident and the DCFO being occupied on other tasks he met oncoming crews and carried out some briefings in the control unit. This appears to have caused confusion to some oncoming crews as to who was the Incident Commander, even though at all times the Incident Commander was appropriately identified.

5.2.18   A series of sectors were identified as the incident was tackled with HFRS officers being assigned to command each one. The majority of comments suggest that the incident command system was not always as described in the Fire Service Manual. This feedback is from HFRS crews, officers and other FRSs.

Incident Commander (white surcoat) consulting industry expert and bronze commanders

Hertfordshire Fire and Rescue Service | Working to Protect. Acting to Save

56

5.2.19 Factors contributing to the issues relating to forward control:

- One of the largest peace time fires in Europe for many years;
- Vast number of responders;
- Variety of "fire" responders;
- Self mobilisation or mobilisation with poor information;
- Varying RVPs;
- No common booking in system;
- Variable levels of familiarity with the "incident command system".

5.2.20 The issues with the ICS can be partly assigned to the scale of the incident and the number of personnel from different FRSs and nationally mobilised teams operating on the site. Sector Commanders were designated, wore tabards, had command support and had communications links to the HFRS Control Unit. Not all personnel were familiar with individual officers. There were occasions when actions were taken by individuals and crews that were not cleared with the chain of command. In the main these were instances that warranted fairly urgent action and were carried out in a professional manner. As with all incidents of this scale there were disagreements and in one instance personnel were committed inside a bund against the advice of Hertfordshire officers.

> **Recommendation 3**
> All local authority FRSs must work to the current edition of the Fire Service Manual on incident command. Other fire responders should be aware of the incident command system and be able to integrate their working practices in order to ensure a safe system of work.

5.2.21 As the incident progressed, sectors were altered to meet the changing needs. During these change over periods there was particular difficulty in informing all crews of all alterations. Following a period of rest, officers returning to the incident were usually allocated to a different role and different sector, so some previously gained knowledge was lost.

Sector Commander in surcoat

5.2.22 There was some confusion on the fireground which was partly due to unfamiliarity with the site. The earlier provision of multiple copies of a simple site plan would have gone someway to dispelling this. From the morning of Tuesday 13th, multiple site plans were provided.

5.2.23 Some functional sectors were set up using New Dimension resources which were mobilised nationally. Those operating within these had to develop on-site command support structures and systems in situ.

5.2.24 Industrial brigades and particularly foam suppliers activated their own emergency response structures. From debrief information these seemed to work well as individual entities. However the interaction between these and HFRS control was limited.

5.3   Procedures

5.3.1   Action plans – The opinion about action plans varied according to the time individuals attended and the role they carried out. Many of the comments received regarding action plans were positive, suggesting that local action plans were communicated to those undertaking operations. However, many personnel were not aware of the overall plan. This was more of a communication issue than a command issue.

5.3.2   The first foam attack, planned on the basis of two fronts operating in phases through the site, was broadly followed. However it continually adapted to meet the changing circumstances. These changes were only communicated to crews in the immediate vicinity.

5.3.3   The incident required dynamic planning on a large scale. As one DO noted,

> "Decision making was always dynamic and under pressure. Although not text book stuff on how it should have been managed it worked well!" HFRS Officer

5.3.4   The key issue on action planning was scale. The Incident, Functional and Sector Commanders did not always appreciate the enormity of individual tasks and the complexity of the whole, especially in planning and preparing for the main foam attack. There was little or no basis on which to make assessments, particularly of timescales. Consequently assessments often needed to be adjusted.

> "The large foam monitors required huge amounts of foam and water before they could be used. Not many people appreciated this and they also didn't understand the enormity of the task to supply them and the time it takes to get the right equipment in place." HFRS Officer

5.3.5   Examples of good action planning include:

- Decision making to mobilise the right resources to tackle the fire;

- Creating a separate incident to deal with the fire at the Northgate building;

- Withdrawing personnel from excessively dangerous situations at critical moments for safety and recommitting them at appropriate times. For example on the afternoon of Monday 12th the integrity of tank 7 was called into question. Further observations on this tank were carried out from the air and as a result two crews were recommitted.

5.3.6   The lack of familiarity with the latest New Dimension equipment (HVP) also required out-of-county personnel to be "very proactive with Sector Officers and Incident Command to get it used when they were confident it could do the job." (Hampshire FRS).

Hertfordshire Fire and Rescue Service | Working to Protect. Acting to Save

58

5.3.7 Inner Cordon - Most debriefs attended or written submissions received identified the initial lack of inner cordon control. Recognisable inner cordon control was put in place on Friday 16th December. The Fire Service Manual states that "Cordons may be employed as an effective method of controlling resources and maintaining safety." (Fire Service Manual, Incident Command, 2002).

> "In the early stages there was little access management and anyone who wanted to turn up could." HFRS Officer

5.3.8 HFRS has crews trained in inner cordon management and specific equipment available; there is no evidence that the procedures of inner cordon management were employed while the bulk of firefighting was taking place. The only exception is the report that one fire fighter was appointed cordon control to monitor persons entering and leaving the site on the afternoon of Sunday 11th December. Despite his best efforts, personnel, from all supporting FRSs and industry, did not appear to adhere to the principles of cordon control.

5.3.9 A series of site withdrawals were required during the incident. There was generally good communication from Sector Commanders to all staff in their sector about possible evacuations and confirmation of the evacuation signal (repeated blasts on whistle). Evacuations from each sector were orderly. However, no head counts were carried out, so evacuation was on a "the area is clear" policy. Between the three FRSs forward controls, New Dimension assets and industrial brigades there was no formal head count or sharing of information.

5.3.10 HFRS uses a system where crew details and officers' keys are attached to their designating tally and placed in the HFRS Control Unit on their entry to the fireground. Although all FRSs have a similar system this particular system is not necessarily replicated nationally. During this incident some HFRS officers considered this system to be carrying out the role of "inner cordon control". Linked to this was the lack of a national identification system for crews, vehicles or individuals. In the event of a roll call being required the lack of a common system could have created additional problems.

5.3.11 Poor personal discipline resulted in some fire personnel entering the risk area without permission and undertaking tasks outside any agreed action plan. It is probable that a reasonably efficient inner cordon would have prevented this.

> **Recommendation 4**
> Structured inner cordon procedures must be implemented and maintained at major incidents.

> **Recommendation 5**
> A national system needs to be established to maintain an accurate record of all fire responders at the scene that will enable a rapid head count if required.

5.3.12 Rendezvous Points (RVPs) - The experience of rendezvous points was time dependent and the even spread of comments received on this issue reflects this. There was good dynamic decision making on the location of RVPs on Sunday morning, following initial assessments of the incident. This enabled sufficient space to be utilised for marshalling.

High Volume Pumping vehicles ready for deployment

5.3.13 The use of the M10 motorway, which is a spur to the M1 close to junction 8, worked well. Despite the resourcing pressures that the police were under, they still escorted on-coming vehicles when required.

> "We arrived at the incident site at 2300 hours where we were met by the local police and placed in a queue." Birmingham International Airport

5.3.14 Later changes in RVPs and in particular the access to them caused some difficulties, in particular for those already in transit to the original RVP. The changes were at times insufficiently communicated to all of organisations that needed to know. Specifically, the variable access available from the M1 motorway confused some out of county resources. Access from the north of the country required vehicles to drive 8 km past the incident and approach from the south. However, some crews stopped at junction 8 of the M1 and removed and replaced the "road closure" to gain access, to discover this access blocked by high volume hose lines.

Crane with HVP

5.3.15 Resources required – Perhaps the largest amount of resources seen at an incident were required for the fire response. These ranged from obvious firefighting equipment and consumables, such as foam and water, to supporting items such as lighting, diesel, hardcore and the services of mechanics. The specific firefighting equipment is discussed in the Appliance, Equipment and Uniforms section.

Hertfordshire Fire and Rescue Service | Working to Protect. Acting to Save

60

5.3.16 Some items were required before further significant firefighting could be undertaken. This included a crane to position HVPs and lighting for the fire ground. These were sourced through various means using partner contacts.

5.3.17 The long lead in times for ordering the large equipment or bulk consumables were not appreciated. There was frustration that resources were not available in the timeframes that personnel were used to at smaller incidents. Many of these frustrations related to diesel and anti-freeze, which were both required in large quantities over a sustained period. It was ironic that there was difficulty in acquiring fuel for appliances and pumps, when the fire was at a fuel depot.

5.3.18 Enabling supplies to pass through the cordon, plus decanting and distribution issues, exacerbated the frustration on receipt. For example the HFRS decanting pump only fits the new Scania appliances. Personnel were not familiar with a considerable volume of equipment. Not all equipment was labelled with fuel type, quantities, re-start procedures, etc.

5.3.19 Efforts were made by many organisations to ensure that their resources on scene could be maintained and minor faults fixed on site. This required the attendance of a mechanic to ensure equipment remained or was rapidly returned to fully functioning capacity.

5.3.20 The lead time to establish supply chains was often longer than was ideal to keep the fire response operating at full potential. This applies to specific equipment such as HVPs (8 hours mobilisation) where it was recognised that a decision to mobilise needed to be taken early, but agreement on the exact number of HVPs required was not determined immediately, resulting in mobilising of 14 HVPs at 17:30 for a 22:00 rendezvous.

5.3.21 The ever changing demand for resources to enable the deployment of HVPs in the Balancing Tank water supply demonstrates many of these issues. The following stages were required:

- Crews to chop down the fences and light vegetation;

Work undertaken at balancing tank to deploy HVP's

- Chainsaw operation for larger branches;

- Several tons of hardcore (type 1), again laid by crews, to build a road;

- Crane to deploy the HVPs as there was insufficient hardcore available from the local authority to complete the road;

- Boat and safety crews to deploy the HVPs in the water.

5.3.22 This was all undertaken in the middle of the night, but as one crew suggested,

> "Decision to build temporary road was left until late into the night. This decision should have been made earlier in the day. Could the army or local authorities not have done this instead of fire crews shovelling type 1?" HFRS crew.

5.3.23 Further resources or services also became urgent as soon as they were identified. These included caterers to supplement the provision made by the voluntary sector. Much of the food and drink was supplied free of charge by the local supermarket, Tesco.

> **Recommendation 6**
> Local Resilience forums should develop a single coordinated centre for the acquisition and distribution of all generic resources for all agencies during major incidents.

5.3.24 **Documentary recording** - There are two positive aspects to be noted in terms of documentary recording. First, that effective documentary recording is recognised amongst the majority of officers as being essential. Secondly, those designated to operate the HFRS Control Unit, who had received some training in log keeping and who had a clear procedure to follow, maintained a well ordered record of the incident for the duration of their involvement.

5.3.25 HFRS Control, FRSNCC and FEIC also had very efficient recording systems. The problems that have arisen post incident have highlighted a number of gaps in the data. This is partly due to:

- Failure or inability to contact HFRS control advising them of vehicle movements;

- Different crews using appliances from other stations and confusion over call signs;

- Switching off the "visual element" of the automatic vehicle location system;

- Crews taking undesignated vehicles.

5.3.26 Events at the fireground are generally well recorded in terms of tactical mode changes with some further detail contained within informatives relayed

62

Hertfordshire Fire and Rescue Service | Working to Protect. Acting to Save to control. At multi-agency commands, formal logs were developed. However these records tend to be unstructured with a very variable standard and format of note taking. For example, there are many loose sheets of paper without a date, time or scribe's name. The rationale behind decision making is rarely recorded making the assessment of the decision making process difficult.

5.3.27 During the incident, the standard of documentary recording lengthened handover periods as there was no rapid way for those deployed to the incident to get up to speed from the logs. In particular there was no simple "decision log" at any of the fire commands for personnel to refer to.

5.3.28 Key issues raised by those required to keep logs were a perceived lack of training, procedure and technology.

> "There must be a way of networking our decision log so that all levels of command are entering data on the same network and can then look at what decisions are made by whom and why." HFRS Officer

> **Recommendation 7**
> HFRS should develop and introduce an efficient and effective recording system for all levels of command. It should provide easy access to the decision log and be supported by appropriate technology and training.

5.4   Personnel

5.4.1   **Specific Task Officers** - This section needs to be read in the context of the scale of the incident. The number of specialist officers who were appointed, or whom personnel felt should have been appointed, were low in comparison to the total deployed. The main difficulties were in identification of functional officers and the complexities of the resourcing.

5.4.2   A number of different issues have been raised in debriefs regarding the allocation of specific task officers.

5.4.3   First, it was difficult to identify those allocated specific tasks, more so in the early stages of the incident. Those that were identified by tabards could often not be located; others were not issued with tabards. This resulted in a lack of broad awareness amongst commanding officers and crews about what specific tasks had been allocated to whom. Consequently, some duplication of task allocation existed, particularly with regards to ordering resources.

5.4.4   Second, during the firefighting phase, there is little evidence of a Safety Officer being appointed on site. The appointment of Safety Officers is one key control measure for reducing risk advised by the Fire Service Manual (Fire Service Operations Incident Command, 2002). The Fire Service Manual sets out the role of Safety Officer(s) as considering specific areas of concern or providing general support to Sector Commanders. It goes as far as suggesting the designation of a Safety Sector in some cases. At this complex event, a series of Safety Officers to survey operational sectors, identify hazards and advise the Sector Commanders or to just provide "an extra set of eyes and ears to the Sector Commanders in monitoring site personnel" (Fire Service Manual 2002) would have been advantageous.

5.4.5 Set against this is the generally high safety culture in all FRSs. Tragically in February 2005 two HFRS firefighters lost their lives while attempting rescues on the 14th floor of a block of flats. As a result HFRS personnel have a very high awareness of risk/benefit factors and will not undertake tasks unless the benefit outcomes are viable. The majority of crews received good health and safety briefings. This issue is covered in more detail in the Health & Safety section.

5.4.6 Third, non-uniformed specialists were under-utilised in areas where their wider skills may have assisted the fire response. This could have included:

- Providing administrative assistance to fire officers at multi-agency commands;

- Supporting the ordering and invoicing of goods and services easing the longer term burden on the finance department;

- Providing regularly updated plans from the drawing office.

5.4.7 Support staff felt that operational officers were too busy to be disturbed and consequently did not offer all available support. This debrief comment was made:

> "During the incident finance staff, I think, could have assisted with some of the queries relating to ordering and paying for goods and services ... this would have released uniformed officers to do what they do best." HFRS Service Accountant

5.4.8 In addition, HFRS officers working in Community Fire Safety could have also been utilised earlier, providing support at multi-agency commands and freeing up further capacity. Community Fire Safety officers were used to supplement ILOs. The finite resource of HFRS officers was more rapidly depleted than if the pool of available resources for support functions had been widened. The result was that on one occasion the number of HFRS officers at the fireground became sufficiently depleted that crews felt they were commanded by out-of-county personnel.

5.4.9 As a further point, it should be noted that officers normally managing support sections of the organisation, by necessity, disappeared from their day jobs. There is no evidence of contingency plans or point of contact for the staff remaining.

5.4.10 Finally, appropriate task officers were appointed to functions at the fireground based on their specialist skills. The key downside to this was that several specialist officers spent longer than normal periods on duty as there were no similarly skilled officers available to relieve them.

Hertfordshire Fire and Rescue Service | Working to Protect. Acting to Save

64

5.4.11   Handovers - The feedback on handovers varied between officers, crews and the roles they carried out. Fire personnel generally felt that the handovers they received were effective, thorough and task focussed.

5.4.12   All officers with sector or functional command roles indicated that they were well-briefed, had a reasonably clear understanding of the wider picture and had sufficient understanding of the issues between sectors and functions. Better written records would have assisted and in all probability speeded up the handover process.

5.4.13 The largest criticism of handovers was from appliance crews in that those deployed to the fireground were not given an overview of events that had occurred or the future action plan. Some of those deployed to a sector had difficulty in identifying the Sector Commander. Hence their handover was given by those they were taking over from, so focussed on specific tasks. This was complicated by the fact that when they arrived at location tasks had changed. This section links strongly to Action Plans.

5.4.14 Those crews deployed in functional supporting sectors considered themselves well briefed on their role but again not on the overview of events that had occurred or the future action plan.

5.4.15 Relief Crews - HFRS Control began by allocating specific crews/ officers to relieve other specific crews/officers. This system did not operate well due to the dynamics of the incident. Oncoming personnel could not find the crew or officer that they were due to relieve. In addition, the tasks requiring personnel were changing rapidly, so it was not always appropriate for one crew to take over from another. In the early stages the timing and allocation of relief crews appeared uncoordinated to those being deployed.

5.4.16 On Monday 12th HFRS Control and the HFRS Control Unit personnel agreed a new system for organising reliefs. HFRS Control would mobilise the agreed number of officers and crews based on the fireground requirements. On arrival at the Control Unit, the oncoming personnel would be allocated tasks and notified of who they were to relieve. This system worked well. The only concern was identifying which crews needed relieving at what times. HFRS Control had this information on their systems and sometimes had to notify the HFRS Control Unit of a crew that had been at the scene for longer than the agreed time.

5.4.17 The majority of the comments received relate to the problems of transporting personnel away from the incident. The majority of these came from HFRS crews, but the same picture was reflected by crews from other FRSs. There was insufficient provision of small scale transport (cars or minibuses) for crews to move around site or away to rest accommodation or their home station.

5.4.18 Some appliances became tied up in the incident, so their crews required alternative transport. They were advised to take another appliance. The knock-on effect of this decision was huge in terms of ongoing logistics and included the following issues:

- Appliances left the incident site with less than the full complement of equipment and a significant time was taken to reallocate or restock these items;

- Crews took vehicles with equipment that they were not familiar with;

- Appliances were not returned to home stations exacerbating the problems for HFRS Control when ensuring county-wide fire cover.

  "I know it was very difficult logistically, but during that week we took home three different appliances." HFRS crew

5.4.19 Over the course of this incident, all HFRS crews and officers were deployed to the incident or to provide cover elsewhere in the county. However, some whole-time crews commented that they were used excessively during the maintenance phase when greater crew rotation could have been employed.

5.4.20 The shift pattern for officers proved problematic due to:

- Locating officers at the incident who were due to be relieved;
- Length of handover times;
- Travel times to incident.

This had a knock on effect on the plans.

5.4.21 The vast majority of retained units have expressed the view that they would benefit from more advanced warning of re-deployment for an extended period of time at such an incident. This would allow more efficient crew management and facilitate the cooperation and assistance of their main employers.

> **Recommendation 8**
> Consideration should be given to providing advance warning of redeployments for an extended period to all crews but particularly retained units.

5.4.22 Despite this, it was rare for a retained crew to be unable to turn out due to lack of riders. The cooperation of main employers was exceptional. The contribution of retained firefighters, coupled with the support of their families, is recognised. (Figure 22).

Type of Appliance	Number of attendances
Retained	179
Wholetime	371

Figure 22
Total attendances of HFRS appliances. 86% of total 642 appliances.

5.4.23 Specialist advice - A broad range of specialist advice was offered during the incident. HFRS was effective in selecting appropriate sources of advice. In

Hertfordshire Fire and Rescue Service | Working to Protect. Acting to Save

66

particular petrochemical firefighting specialists were requested and proved invaluable. At the fireground their advice was crucial in developing tactical plans and making decisions regarding strategic withdrawals. Their expertise as advisors, particularly in the calculation of foam requirements was invaluable. Critically, they were able to communicate relatively complex information in a clearly understandable manner.

5.4.24 At the suggestion of Essex FRS, a private company called SembCorp Utilities Ltd were requested to attend as they had specialist equipment for tackling pressure fed fires.

"SembCorp's emergency response team were requested to provide immediate support to the firefighting activity on the fireground with the existing Total and BP firefighters and equipment under the control of the Incident Commander. ... The SembCorp ERT and equipment was deployed and fully utilised ..." SembCorp Utilities Ltd debrief report

5.4.25 Essex County FRS provided a number of experienced personnel to operate their foam equipment. Their previous large-scale major foam attack exercises had reinforced the need for a number of trained specialist officers.

5.4.26 Specialists with knowledge and equipment were forthcoming from a range of sources. For example, Bedfordshire and Luton FRS provided officers with air sampling equipment on Wednesday 14th and Thursday 15th to assist in the identification of explosive atmospheres. London Fire Brigade scientific advisors also attended.

5.4.27 Many personnel at the fireground gave some instruction on equipment unfamiliar to other personnel. This was greatly beneficial, allowing a task to be continued even when specialist personnel were on a rest period away from the fireground.

5.4.28 The flow of information from the site operators improved as the incident progressed. Access to on site information proved impossible due to the destruction of the site control centre. Despite this, the site operators were very supportive during the firefighting phase, providing significant information and assistance at the fireground and multi-agency commands.

5.4.29 A site recovery team was set up on Monday 12th December. However, following the stop message, on Wednesday 14th, progress stalled in this area. There was early confusion about site responsibility and the timings of handing over authority, and who had responsibility for what.

5.4.30 A range of comments were received regarding specialist advice. Negative comments relate to specific time periods and interaction with specific organisations. In particular, it was felt that health protection advice for emergency responders at the fireground (and for the public) was not available in a timely and accessible manner. The advice given on the smoke plume was that it would be over northern France and Luxembourg and heading for Germany by mid afternoon on Monday 12th and all those below the plume with respiratory conditions should "go in, stay in and tune in". Considerable regard was given to the air pollution advice received when making strategic fire decisions. In reality, the smoke plume over France was at a high level and only in the northwest tip, so the impact on the population was significantly less than was understood by the recipients of the information.

5.4.31 HFRS also experienced some difficulty in communicating with the Environment Agency. The EA had a range of issues and long term implications to consider. Therefore, it is understandable that it was necessary to consider issues beyond the immediate firefighting, in terms of long term impacts to the environment. However, the time taken to complete these communications was lengthy and resulted in some frustration on behalf of the FRS. Both organisations recognise and understand that there are different drivers to consider whilst dealing with complex situations such as Buncefield.

5.4.34 **Sufficient Orders** - The majority view is that sufficient orders were given for the necessary levels of command. Many of these were conveyed during specific handovers. HFRS crews in particular were clear on the tasks to be undertaken within their sector. Confusion arose between rather than within sectors, sometimes giving the perception that other fire responders, in particular, were working independently. On reflection, this is most likely to be a perception rather than the reality, arising as a result of communication difficulties at the incident.

Oil industry firefighter in action

Hertfordshire Fire and Rescue Service | Working to Protect. Acting to Save

68

5.4.35 Out-of-county personnel had a less positive experience of command. In particular, those deployed without a senior officer to liaise directly with HFRS were less clear on their remit.

5.4.36 A number of comments have been received relating to the variability and performance of operational officers in relation to incident command skills. The vast majority of officers commanded well, but there was a perceived lack of active decision making amongst others.

5.4.37 Away from the fireground officers undertaking unfamiliar tasks occasionally required clarification on their levels of responsibility in particular in relation to engaging external support and committing HFRS financially.

Massive plume of smoke visible over the South East of England

Figure 24
Map of buildings
assessed and
searched

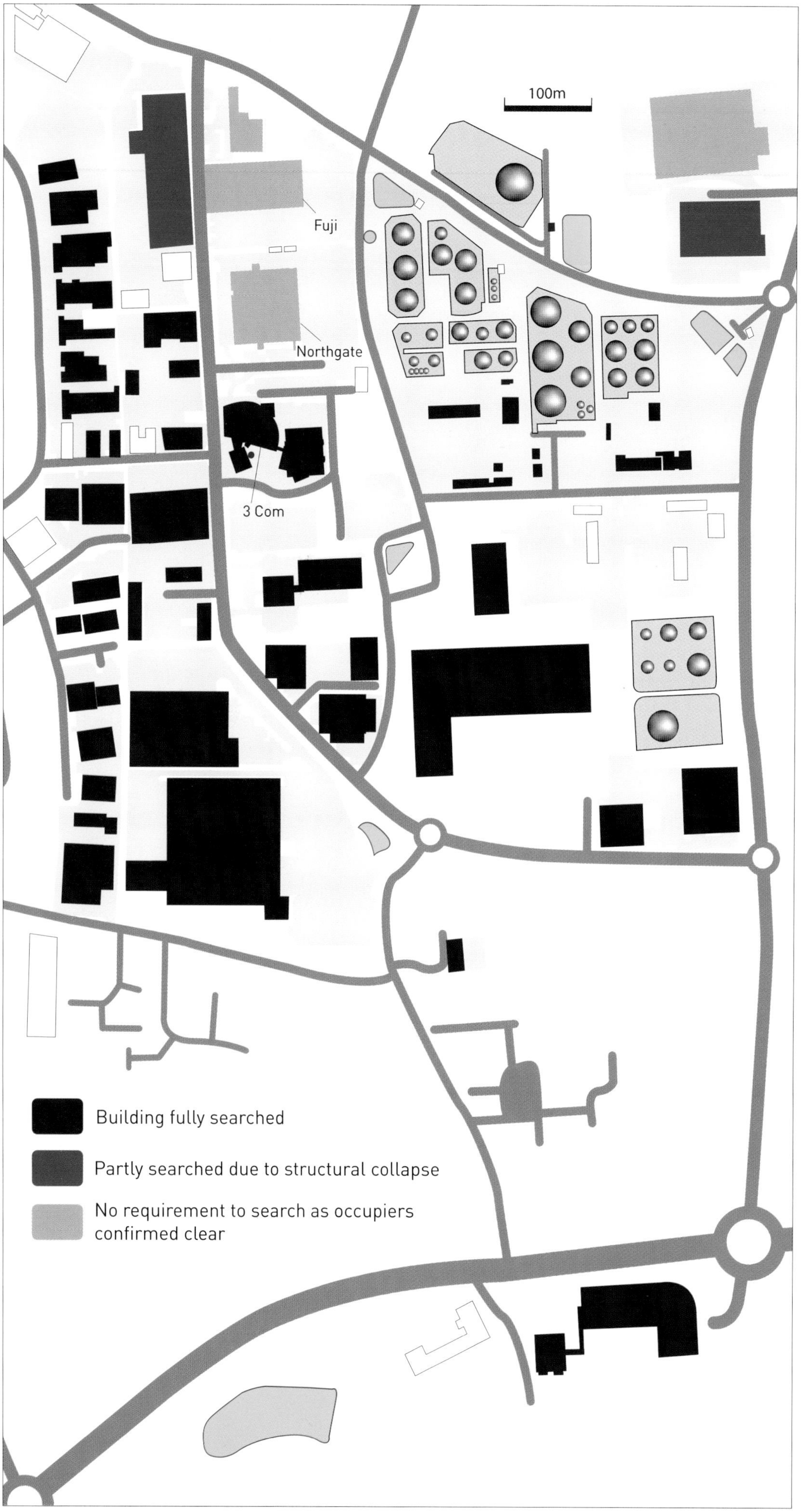

100m

Fuji

Northgate

3 Com

Building fully searched

Partly searched due to structural collapse

No requirement to search as occupiers
confirmed clear

Hertfordshire Fire and Rescue Service | Working to Protect. Acting to Save

70

6 Fireground and Functional Sectors

6.1 Overview

6.1.1 This section looks at the way in which the incident was commanded at Fire Silver and Bronze levels. In addition to HFRS, 31 other Local Authority FRSs and five industrial brigades attended this incident. As an example London Fire Brigade provided a total of 65 appliance attendances during the fire.

6.1.2 The key issues that have arisen through debriefs are marshalling and delivering sufficient resources to the fireground and minimising the environmental impact of the fire response. The main issues relating to forward control, inner cordons, RVPs and handovers are noted in the Incident Command section of this report.

6.2 Search and rescue

6.2.1 The key factor that made the search and rescue operation successful was the multi-agency approach to gathering and sharing information. With the police leading the coordination on missing persons and constantly updating HFRS, the task of prioritising resources to "sectors" was carried out more efficiently.

Figure 23
Map of sectors

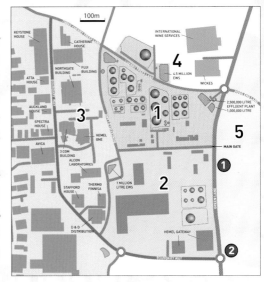

6.2.2 The incident was initially sectorised into five (figure 23), with sector 5 quickly disbanded. Sectors 1, 2 and 4 had few significant properties in them. The main search and rescue focus was in sector 3. Approximately 53 buildings covering an area approximately 1.5 km by 1 km were assessed in detail, 47 were searched and four partially searched. Occupiers informed HFRS that all persons had been accounted for in the remaining two buildings (Figure 24).

11/12/2005
08:02:58 Informative APPROX 20 TANKS BELIEVED INVOLVED IN FIRE - BLAST DAMAGE OVER A LARGE AREA - SEARCH IN PROGRESS OF AREAS AND BUILDINGS - NO FIREFIGHTING ACTION TM DELTA

11/12/2005
09:20:00 Informative AS PREVIOUS INFORMATIVE-NUMEROUS FIRES AND BLAST DAMAGE-IN SURROUNDING AREAS OF BOUNDARY

LANE AND MAYLANDS AVENUE-FURTHER SEARCHES IN PROGRESS-NO FIREFIGHTING ACTIONS-TM DELTA

11/12/2005
14:13:35 Informative CHECKS ON ADJACENT BUILDINGS AND POLICE LIAISONS HAVE IDENTIFIED 10 PERSONS UNACCOUNTED FOR. SEVERAL BUILDINGS ARE IN A DANGEROUS CONDITION - POLICE REQUESTING KEYHOLDERS .

6.2.3 A number of key decisions were made fairly early on the Sunday morning. The Incident Commander did not request specialised search and rescue teams. This decision took into account:

- The day of the week, time and the location of the incident, which was mainly centred within the light industrial/business area of the town;

- Information being received from the police;

- Direct witness testimony from security guards and other staff at various locations;

- Information being relayed back from the sectors.

6.2.4 The deployment of national urban search and rescue teams would have placed an unnecessary burden on an already stretched command system.

6.2.5 Search and rescue was commenced by the first crews on arrival at sector 3, this has already been discussed in the Incident section. The principles of working outwards from the point of greatest danger applied throughout. The Northgate building was the first to be partially searched, followed by the Fuji building just to the north. This was carried out by the crews from St Albans and Redbourn. The interior of the Northgate building was described as follows, "It looked as if you had picked it up, shaken it on its side and then put it back down very carefully" (HFRS crew). Fire crews are of the opinion that had the building been occupied there was every prospect of multiple fatalities and serious injuries. This was the case in a number of the buildings.

Devastation. Fuji building in the foreground with Catherine House in the distance.

Hertfordshire Fire and Rescue Service | Working to Protect. Acting to Save

72

6.2.6 Shortly after 07:30 the officers in attendance quickly coordinated a north to south search using the six pumps available in sector 3 at that time. The majority of the most severely damaged buildings backed onto the Buncefield depot. Due to the security staff being located at the front of these buildings they avoided serious injury.

6.2.7 Due to the very visible, severe structural damage and highly compacted nature of internal furnishings the Sector Commander decided that survivability was minimal and crews would not be committed to some buildings.

6.2.8 Considerable effort was made in searching the 3 Com building as information had been received that there were 10 persons unaccounted for from this building. Although no persons could be located there was strong visual evidence that personal injuries had occurred. At 16:12 the police received multiple repeat 999 emergency calls that they traced to the 3 Com building. They were unable to speak to anyone at the originating end. A fire appliance was dispatched to the scene and was unable to locate the phone or any casualties. It is thought that these repeat calls were caused by a technical fault.

6.3 Cooling

Cooling jets cover tankers at the loading gantry

6.3.1 Early discussions with site staff confirmed that the majority of tanks contained product which would slow heating such that cooling did not need to be commenced immediately. The first appliances at the depot set in to the Million Litre emergency water supply (EWS) at the south west corner of the site as early as 08:00. At 11:07 the first covering sprays and cooling jets were run out, but not yet charged, in order  to cover the tanker loading gantry area and HOSL bunds D and E. These were charged shortly after midday. This was followed by the application of cooling jets to the BPA bund, specifically tanks 4 and 7, and the HOSL east bund (Figure 13). A total of 14 lines of 70mm and two of 45mm hose were run out, supplying 13 monitors and using nearly 200 lengths of hose.

> 11/12/2005
> 11:12:48 Informative AS PREVIOUS-STEADY PROGRESS IN SEARCHING AREAS SURROUNDING BOUNDARY WAY, MAYLANDS AVE AND THREE CHERRY TREES LANE-FIRES UNDER CONTROL IN THESE AREAS-COOLING JETS BEING LAID OUT AROUND PERIMETER OF TANK FARM-CALCULATIONS FOR FOAM ATTACK IN PROGRESS-TM DELTA

Tank 902
glowing

11/12/2005
16:04:33 Informative   AS PREVIOUS INFORMATIVE - 22 TANKS
BELIEVED FULLY INVOLVED - MAJOR COOLING ON A FURTHER 7
TANKS - STEADY PROGRESS BEING MADE - CREWS EVACUATED
FROM SITE - PROGRESS BEING MADE IN PREPARATION FOR FOAM
ATTACK - GAS SUPPLY ISOLATED - TM TANGO

11/12/2005
17:32:58 Informative   AS PREVIOUS INFORMATIVE FOAM
EQUIPMENT BEING LAID OUT TO TACKLE PERIPHERAL AREAS OF
TANK AND BUND FIRES MAJOR WATER SUPPLY LOCATED READY
FOR HIGH VOLUME PUMPERS SILVER COMMAND INFORMED BULK
FOAM SUPPLY INCREASED TO 170,000 LITRES COOLING JETS STILL
IN PLACE FIRST STAGE FOAM ATTACK PLANNED FOR 19.00 HRS TM
TANGO

11/12/2005
20:54:20 Informative   AS PREVIOUS INFORMATIVE STEADY
PROGRESS BEING MADE WITH COOLING, COOLING JETS
REPOSITIONED 1 TANK RIM SEAL FOAMED STILL AWAITING FULL
FOAM ARRIVAL MAIN WATER SUPPLY BEING ESTABLISHED USING
HIGH VOLUME PUMPS MAJOR LIGHTING BEING POSITIONED
TACTICAL FOAM ATTACK PLAN BEING ORGANISED ENVIRONMENT
AGENCY AND THAMES WATER ADVISED ON POSSIBLE FOAM RUN
OFF TM TANGO

12/12/2005
13:56:35 Informative   TANK NO.5 HEAVILY INVOLVED IN FIRE -
AFFECTING TANK NO. 7 - FOAM ATTACK ON NO.5 - 6 GROUND
MONITORS COOLING TANK 7 - ALL CREWS BEING WITHDRAWN TO
SAFE DISTANCE - ALL RUNNING FUEL FIRES CONTAINED IN BUND
- SPOT FIRE IN OTHER BUNDS BEING ATTACKED WITH FOAM - TM
OSCAR

Hertfordshire Fire and Rescue Service | Working to Protect. Acting to Save

74

12/12/2005
17:16:31 Informative   FOLLOWING REVIEWED RISK ASSESSMENT
FROM POLICE HELICOPTER DOWN LINK REGARDING 5 AND 7 - TWO
CREWS INTRODUCED TO MAINTAIN COOLING JETS AND RUN OFF -
T M OSCAR

12/12/2005
18:29:11 Informative   LIMITED FIREFIGHTING OPERATIONS IN
PROGRESS - COOLING OF UNAFFECTED TANKS VIA 3 GROUP
MONITORS - T M OSCAR

12/12/2005
20:49:03 Informative   3 SECTORS IN OPERATION - COOLING OF ALL
UNAFFECTED TANKS IN PROGRESS USING 3 GROUND MONITORS
AND 2 TITAN MONITORS - WATER FROM BUNDED AREAS BEING
REDISTRIBUTED - 9 HIGH VOLUME PUMPS IN RELAY FOR FIRE
FIGHTING REMOVING EXCESS WATER FROM TREATMENT COMPLEX
TO AVOID CONTAMINATION OF WATER COURSES - FURTHER
ASSESSMENT OF WATER SUPPLIES IN PROGRESS - TM OSCAR

13/12/2005
00:04:32 Informative   COOLING BEING CARRIED OUT ON TANK 7 -
WATER SPRAY IN AVIATION AREA - DIVERTING WATER FROM
LOADING AREA FOR MANIFOLD NEXT TO TANK 4 - TANK 4
RUPTURED EFFORTS BEING MADE TO PROTECT TANK 7 PLUS
SURROUNDING AREA - TM OSCAR

13/12/2005 0
2:44:42 Informative   FURTHER COOLING JETS ESTABLISHED - RUN
OFF CONTROL BEING ENHANCED - WATER CONTAINMENT PLAN
BEING DEVISED - TM OSCAR

13/12/2005
04:08:16 Informative AS PREVIOUS - COOLING CONTINUING -
DEVELOPING NEXT PHASE OF FOAM ATTACK -
ELECTRICITY CONFIRMED ISOLATED - GOLD INFORMED - TM OSCAR

6.3.2   During debriefs there were a number of out of county personnel who
expressed a view that cooling should have been commenced at an earlier
stage. Poor horizontal communications between all of the organisations and
vertically within individual organisations resulted in some confusion over the
action plan.

6.3.3   The cooling jets and the quantity of water being applied into the bunds
were constantly monitored. There is one recorded instance of a bund
"overtopping" due to excess fluid. When this occurred on Monday 12th it was
one of the main factors that prompted the decision to increase resources to 25
pumps.

6.3.4   A constant balance had to be maintained between available resources,
both personnel and water. HFRS appliances were pumping from the Million
Litre EWS at near maximum capacity from late on Sunday morning through to

late afternoon on Wednesday 14th. These pumps largely supplied the cooling jets at about 600,000 litres per hour.

Water cooling application

6.3.5 There is little doubt that the cooling operations combined with the Sunday evening preventative foam attacks kept the fire spread to a minimum.

6.4 Marshalling of resources

6.4.1 The marshalling of resources can be considered successful. Sufficient resources were available to commence the first major foam attack only 26 hours after ignition. The effort required to achieve this was significant, particularly in relation to getting the correct foam concentrate, in the correct vehicle to the foam production site.

6.4.2 The marshalling caused some early problems, associated with the location of RVPs and the access route from the M1, but these were largely resolved by Monday.

6.4.3 The location of the three control units (HFRS, London, and Essex) caused some initial confusion to the majority of external responders. These external responders were not familiar with any of the units or the personnel who crewed them. In cases where there had been confusion over national access routes and RVPs, the co-location of the control units served to strengthen opinion on the robustness of the command system in place.

6.4.4 During the early part of the incident, resources became confused as vehicles and equipment built up without adequate tracking or parking systems (Figure 25).

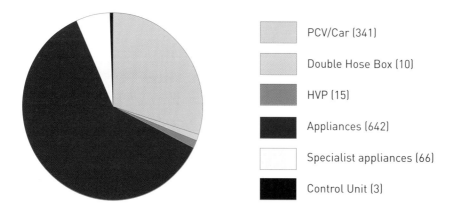

PCV/Car (341)

Double Hose Box (10)

HVP (15)

Appliances (642)

Specialist appliances (66)

Control Unit (3)

Figure 25
Chart of all resources

Prior to the deployment of the HVPs for the foam attack on the Monday morning the dual carriageway, Breakspear Way, had to be cleared. Although this issue is covered elsewhere in this report it is worth reiterating that the simple basics of reception, logging and key control would have assisted. It is also worth noting that there are no national procedures to follow.

Hertfordshire Fire and Rescue Service | Working to Protect. Acting to Save

76

> **Recommendation 9**
> A national procedure for the reception, logging and key control of vehicles at incidents involving multiple fire responders should be developed.

6.4.5   There is a national procedure for large out of county convoy deployment that a number of FRSs attempted to implement. This procedure includes requesting a police escort. The police were either not requested or when requested explained that it would be difficult due to their current commitments. Hertfordshire Constabulary provided good in county escorts.

6.4.6   Practical problems encountered with the convoys included blinding by the rear blue lights of the vehicle in front and actually keeping the convoy as a convoy.

> "Prime movers are fitted with rear repeaters at chassis level, which can't be turned off. When travelling in convoy for long distances this causes the following drivers to become blinded. There is a need to install an override switch to allow the repeaters to be isolated."
> Somerset debrief report

6.5   Planning

6.5.1   The overarching plan of an attack on two fronts progressing in a phased way through the site was put into action with only minor changes. All main fires were extinguished within 60 hours of the first major attack. Both facts strongly suggest that the planning was effective.

6.5.2   Normal methods were used in planning, with consideration of the additional issues raised by a major incident. Planning drew on the local expertise that has built up over the years and the work undertaken in pre-planning. All personnel at all levels had to draw heavily on previous operational experience not only to develop initial plans but to constantly review and adapt them to changing circumstances. Functional and Sector Commanders, company representatives on site, multi-agency partners and commands all provided direct feedback which fed into further iterations of the plan. As ever the main problem was in prioritising, categorising and ensuring that information was appropriately devolved.

6.5.3   Planning commenced on the Sunday morning when the CFO in gold command ordered the DCFO to "put the fire out". A significant amount of time was needed to develop a comprehensive plan (Figure 23). Major planning meetings, chaired by the DCFO, were held in the Essex County FRS Control Unit, which provided a quiet and functional area. These meetings were used to confirm and update the planning process.

6.5.4   The more specific issues relating to water and foam are covered later in this section.

6.5.5   During the planning phase, the main issues were:

- Considering the environmental impact.

- Difficulty in assessing the complexity of tasks;

- Under-estimation of the time needed to complete tasks due to the size and uniqueness;

- Multi-agency agreements took longer to broker than expected;

6.5.6   These resulted in a number of "false starts" for the first major foam attack which had the potential to cause confusion. Clear communication of the delays relayed by the HFRS personnel at the multi-agency commands prevented a loss of confidence in the fire response.

6.5.7   Initial calculations for the duration of the foam attack were too conservative. The predicted requirements of foam, water, crews, etc were underestimated and had to be continually updated.

6.6   Water

6.6.1   Despite the loss of the internal fire main to the site and very limited access to the on-site emergency water supplies, an extended and coordinated water supply to the fire was sustained throughout the incident.

6.6.2   The three on site fire main pump houses had been destroyed along with significant sections of pipe work. The only accessible emergency water supply was the Million Litre EWS in the south west corner of the site.

6.6.3   Five main off-site water supplies were considered (Figure 26).

- The River Ver, 5 km from the site, but reported to be dry by the EA;

- The balancing tank approximately 2 km to the north of the site, but reported dry by the police;

- A lake in St Albans about 6 km away, but this had a head of about 54m;

- The Grand Union Canal in Hemel Hempstead, about 6 km distance but with a head of about 54m;

Figure 26
Potential water
sources

- The Breakspear Way "Balancing Tank", 1.8 km southwest with a head of 9m.

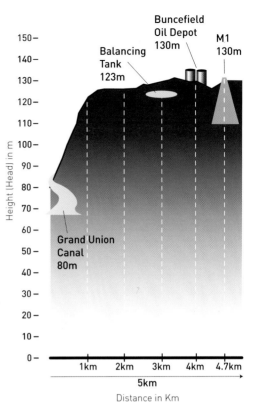

6.6.4 When selected as the major water supply the actual access to the Balancing Tank (Breakspear Way) was difficult and time consuming. Crews were used for a variety of tasks such as cutting down fences, hedges and trees and laying the road. Some feedback has indicated that these crews felt that they could have been more gainfully employed at the fireground.

6.6.5 The New Dimension HVP tactical advisor arrived at multi-agency silver at 13:30 on Sunday 11th December and began to brief HFRS officers on the capabilities of HVPs. This included the use of specialised software to calculate the requirements of different proposals. At 17:30 HFRS requested the mobilisation of 14 HVPs plus water rescue crews essential for their safe deployment in the Balancing Tank.

Recommendation 10

Each fire main pump house and emergency water supply should be positioned and/or constructed such that they cannot be affected by foreseeable incidents. Sufficient hard standing should be provided for the maximum number of mobile pumps that might be expected.

Off site water supplies and their access should be taken into consideration during the pre-planning phase for forseeable incidents at facilities of this type.

Recommendation 11

Early consideration needs to be given to the type, quantity and duration of deployment of national resources.

Recommendation 12

A team of HVP national operational and tactical advisers should be trained and equipped to be deployed anywhere in the U.K.. Consideration should also be given to extending this to all National ND resources.

6.6.6 A number of comments have been received that HVP crews had varying levels of experience. This is not surprising given that the pumps are new in service and this was the first significant national deployment.

"Liaison between individual HVP crews was found to be poor due to an absence of effective sector command and variances in crew practice and levels of competence. Where crews operated within their own brigade operating procedures, this was found to be satisfactory but could not be collectively attributed to a sector fire plan." Royal Berkshire debrief report

6.6.7 By Wednesday an additional five HVPs from the Fire Service College had been sent to FRSs across the country as strategic reserves. This enabled a national operational capability to be maintained.

6.6.8 One HVP was utilised onsite from the initial attendance until the 28th December and recovered on 30th December. It was left under the control of HFRS. Royal Berkshire FRS HVP instructors trained some nominated HFRS personnel to operate the HVP while it was deployed in water. This included instruction on how to stop, start,

HVP equipment

pump, refuel, check oil levels and recognise fault warnings. Arrangements were set up to recall Royal Berkshire FRS if the HVP required moving.

"This was a very successful resolution to a potentially difficult situation over the Christmas period and was due to the close co-operation between Royal Berkshire FRS and HFRS". HVP Report

6.6.9 One of the main areas of discussion and multi-agency agreement centred around the HV hose run from the Balancing Tank to the fireground. There were insufficient HV hose ramps to allow the hose to be laid and then crossed. Any road closure due to HV hose would have been in place for a number of days. There were two options, close either the M1 or the access to the town. The main factor was access/egress routes from the incident site, but consideration was given to the general impact on the incident, including the location of hotels to allow crews to rest. The route shown in figure 27 was selected, thereby keeping open a continuous access and egress route for the site.

Hose run

Hertfordshire Fire and Rescue Service | Working to Protect. Acting to Save

80

Figure 27
Actual route of
HVP hose

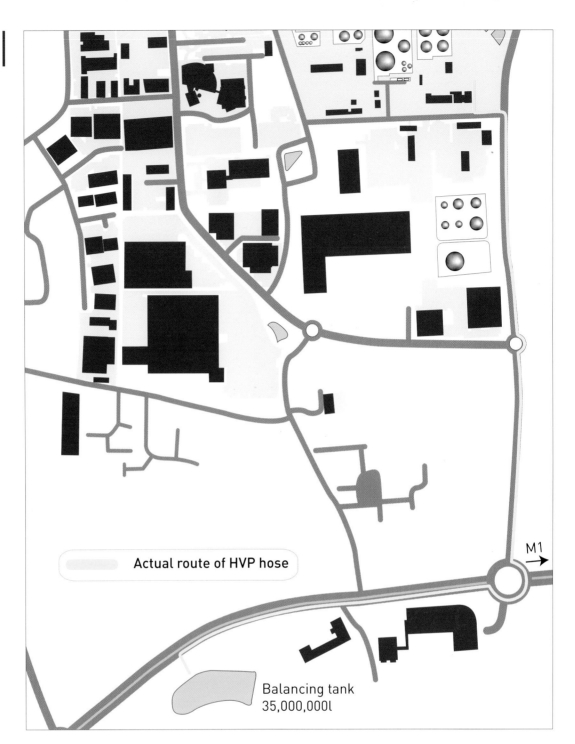

Actual route of HVP hose

Balancing tank
35,000,000l

M1
→

6.6.10 Managing the water supply and run off was one of the most significant issues that had to be addressed (Figure 28). The supply of firefighting water to the site was regularly shut down. During these shut downs opportunities were taken to reposition equipment.

6.6.11 HFRS and the EA continually liaised in an effort to ensure that run off did not occur, or if it did, that the effects were mitigated. During Sunday 11th the water used for cooling was allowed to run into the normal site drainage system.

6.6.12 In initial discussions with the EA the Incident Commander discussed the possibility of emptying the relatively clean, pre-incident contents from the effluent plant onto adjacent fields. The EA determined that the risk of contamination from this water was too great. Consequently the distribution of

Location and Reason	Type and No. of pumps.	No. and size (mm) of hose lines	Approx distance covered km	Delivery Point	Approx qty of water pumped
Million litre EWS to sector 1 for cooling jets and foam. EWS refilled by town main	Fire appliances at 2,2501 lpm	11 x 70mm 2 x 45mm	0.5 0.25	To HOSL bunds A, D, E, Tanker Gantry area. BPA Bund.	20 million litres
Breakspear Way Balancing Tank to Booster site 1 pre withdraw. Refilled from town mains.	6 HVP *	12 X 150mm	1.8	12 to Booster Site 1.	
Booster site 1 within Oil Depot .	3 HVP	6 X 150mm	0.4	3 to the Six Gun Foam Monitor. 1 to a Foam Generator appliance via manifold. 2 terminated in manifolds unused.	33 million litres
Breakspear Way Balancing Tank to Booster site 1 post withdraw.	6 HVP	12 X 150mm	1.8	6 to Booster Site 2. 6 Bypass Booster site 2 to gate valves at entrance. (1 to manifold, 5 unused)	
Booster site 2 at roundabout	3 HVP	6 X 150mm	0.8	1 to Patriot Foam Monitor. 2 to Six Gun Foam Monitor. 3 to gate valves at entrance unused.	
Effluent Plant	4 HVP	7 X 150mm	0.3	5 to HOSL bund, 1 to BP bund to prevent run off. 1 to manifold feeding covering monitors between BPA & hosl	15 million litres
BP Bund	1 HVP	1 X 150mm	0.5	1 to Effluent Plant to feed covering monitors between BPA & HOSL.	Unknown
Million Litre EWS	2 HVP	2 X 150mm	0.5	1 to APL via manifold. 1 to Patriot Foam Monitor.	Unknown
4.5 Million Litre EWS	1 HVP	1 X 150mm	0.5	Firstly to the BP bund then from the BPA bund.	Unknown

* HVP pumping capacity 7,000 lpm

Figure 28
Table of water pumped.

Hertfordshire Fire and Rescue Service | Working to Protect. Acting to Save

82

water to unaffected parts of the site was considered. It was accepted that considerable additional resources would be required to ensure that any possible land and water table contamination was contained on site or at worst minimised. A plan was established to keep all fluids contained on the site.

6.6.13 To accommodate the estimated run off from the foam attack, the contents of the effluent plant were pumped into bunds on the HOSL East site using three HVPs.

Aerial photograph showing the High Volume Pumping equipment on site near the effluent plant

6.6.14 However, the integrity of the bund wall was in question, so a further distribution system was set up to pump this water to the unaffected BP site. HFRS had originally been informed that these bunds had no capacity, but observations by HFRS officers confirmed both BP bunds could receive water.

6.6.15 The liaison with the water companies worked well. Following close consultation with company representatives, sufficient water was provided from the town mains to keep both the Million Litre EWS topped up and the Balancing Tank sufficiently full. Again cooperation ensured that neither of these supplies overfilled.

6.7 Foam

6.7.1   The main considerations for foam concentrate were:

- What was required?
- From where?
- How to get it effectively to the fireground?

The fact that the "FIRE ALL OUT" message was sent on Thursday lunchtime demonstrates how well the foam plan worked.

Foam monitor in use

6.7.2 The initial calculations on the quantity of foam concentrate focused on the amount required to extinguish an area approximately 100m by 100m and maintain the blanket for a short period. This figure was rounded up to allow for error and doubled to allow for maintenance of the blanket. The 300,000 litres estimated was 44% of 786,000 litres actually used over the 26 days that HFRS were at the site.

6.7.3   The FRSNCC were requested to carry out a national survey of all foam and lighting in all FRSs in England, Scotland and Wales, any other military, industrial sites or airports that could have resources which could be released. Of the 58 FRSs surveyed, 49 responded that they could release foam and/or equipment. Time was taken to consider resilience should a second incident occur. The FRSs with significant airports, military or industrial sites within their boundaries received positive responses from 30 of these sources.

6.7.4   During the Sunday morning there was insufficient knowledge of the foam issues and at that time robust dialogue had not been opened with the relevant experts. The request made via FRSNCC was deliberately broad so as not to exclude anything that could have been available.

6.7.5   In one local authority FRS the command and control systems allowed all of their foam tenders to be mobilised out of area without automatically prompting the Control Operator. This concern was noted when the operator sought authorisation for an external deployment from the duty Principal Officer and not all the foam tenders were released.

> ### Recommendation 13
> Local and national assessments of the likelihood of further incidents should be undertaken prior to the release of FRS resources under national mutual aid.

Hertfordshire Fire and Rescue Service | Working to Protect. Acting to Save

84

6.7.6 The vast majority of the foam came from a single industrial supplier, Angus Fire. Angus had first contacted HFRS on Sunday 11th at 07:21 asking if they knew what they needed. Until this single main supplier arrangement became embedded on the Monday, there was some confusion relating to the supply of foam. At the same time unordered foam was arriving from many sources.

6.7.7 The position improved as the incident progressed and it must be stressed that at no time did the incident run out of foam.

6.7.8 Angus Fire supplied over 600,000 litres of foam concentrate from Sunday 11th with the last delivery arriving on 24th December. During the initial supply period the Department for Transport gave limited exemption to specified tanker drivers that allowed them to exceed their normal driving hours.

6.7.9 There was unfamiliarity with the broad range of foam production and application equipment that had arrived from around the country. Ground monitors and hand held branches or pourers were relatively simple in operation but still required a degree of on the job familiarisation.

"Specialist foam equipment and training of relief crews on the job was a little fraught." (HFRS Officer)

6.7.10 All firefighters understood the principles of foam application. Due to environmental considerations the live application of foam in training has largely been replaced by simulation. On occasions during the incident the application of foam could have been carried out more efficiently. The balance between cooling and maintaining the foam blanket was not clearly understood by all personnel.

6.7.11 HFRS crews operated the Titan monitors that were supplied by the site. Firefighters from industry brigades and other Local Authority FRSs operated their specialised equipment and were supported by HFRS crews. In the main this was a very effective use of resources. It would have been virtually impossible to have safely and efficiently extinguished this fire without the experience and close cooperation of all fire and industry attendees.

Industrial fire appliance applying foam

6.7.12 Quite correctly, assumptions were made that those with specialised equipment would have a higher level of knowledge on which to base their operational risk assessments. There was one notable exception when firefighters were committed inside a bund. This was done without the knowledge of the Sector Commander. It is worth highlighting this single, exceptional deviation from standard practices.

6.7.13 Occasional interruptions to the water supply stopped foam from being applied. During some of the interruptions the opportunity was taken to reposition major foam making equipment to better locations.

6.8   Withdrawals

6.8.1   It is clear from all of the debriefs that personnel were safely withdrawn whenever this was required (Figure 29). All personnel understood and reacted to the evacuation signal of short sharp blasts on a whistle.

Date	Time	Reason	Sector
Sunday 11th	13:48	Possible tank collapse	2
Sunday 11th	15:00	Possible tank collapse	2
Monday 12th	13:39	Possible tank collapse & crews surrounded by fire	2
Monday 12th	14:05	Possible tank collapse & crews surrounded by fire	All (on site)
Monday 12th	22:26	Possible tank collapse	All (on site)
Tuesday 13th	00:01	Possible tank collapse	1

Figure 29
Table of partial and full withdrawals

6.8.2   When the Fire Silver Command received advice, usually from industry experts, that the structural integrity of a tank could not be guaranteed, a withdrawal was ordered without consultation with the Sector Commanders. Sector Commanders and crews were not always aware of the reason for the withdrawal and this caused frustration on the fireground.

6.8.3   In most cases Sector Commanders had pre-selected appropriate, safe egress routes. Sectors were checked to confirm that all personnel had withdrawn. Some informal head counts took place, but there is no evidence that these were collated and confirmed. This would have been difficult as:

- Crews were re-tasked by other crews or Sector Commanders;

- Operational and functional sectors became blurred on the complex and dynamic fireground;

Hertfordshire Fire and Rescue Service | Working to Protect. Acting to Save

86

- Withdrawals were not communicated to all personnel outside the specific sector being withdrawn (so those deployed elsewhere would not report for a roll call).

6.8.4   During withdrawals the vast majority of equipment was left to operate unattended. Only equipment that required constant monitoring or operation – such as foam tenders – was shut down.

6.8.5   Returns to work commenced following a further risk assessment, based on joint industry and FRSs observations, often supported by an aerial view. They are recorded in the tactical mode within informatives.

> 12/12/2005
> 17:16 Informative   FOLLOWING REVISED RISK ASSESSMENT FROM POLICE HELICOPTER DOWN LINK REGARDS TANK 5 AND 7. 2 CREW RE-INTRODUCED TO MAINTAIN COOLING JETS AND RUN OFF CONTROL. T/M OSCAR

6.8.6   A combination of poor communication and discipline resulted in some non-HFRS personnel returning into the risk area prior to a return being agreed or announced.

6.9   Maintenance Phase

6.9.1   The maintenance phase, with a multitude of emerging issues, proved to be as time consuming and in some ways as difficult as the firefighting phase. It lasted until 5th January 2005.

6.9.2   The plan for recovery and longer term consequences were first discussed at the multi-agency gold command meeting at 01:00 on Monday 12th.

> "Need to resolve issues like clearing out the water from the site or do we ask the owners to take part." Multi-agency gold minutes 12/12/2006 01:00

6.9.3   There was good cooperation with site representatives throughout the firefighting phase, commencing at 07:20 on Sunday 11th with the first supervisor liaising with forward control. During the maintenance phase, this close liaison and cooperation continued at all levels. However from an HFRS perspective, there seemed to be confusion about who the lead authority on site should be as the incident progressed into one of monitoring and maintaining, particularly with regard to water run off. Hertfordshire's CFO contacted the Office of the Deputy Prime Minister on 21st December to try to resolve the issue.

6.9.4   From 15th December until 3rd January, HFRS chaired the site recovery group and continued to work on site over Christmas. HFRS last attended the site on 5th January when control was handed back to site operators.

6.9.5 There were a wide range of issues to be addressed following the maintenance phase:

- Clearing the main roads and relocating HFRS Control Unit to the site;
- Maintaining the foam blanket;
- Monitoring the temperature of liquids on site;
- Monitoring the atmosphere for flammability levels;
- Arranging for the collection and return of national assets;
- Cleaning and certifying cleanliness of HVPs;
- Returning HFRS appliances to their correct stations;
- Reuniting HFRS equipment with the correct appliance.

6.9.6 One of the national issues that arose was in certifying the cleanliness of HVP hose and equipment. High pressure steam washers were eventually used. However, due to differing local standards and procedures not all FRSs accepted that their HVPs were sufficiently clean. Some local arrangements were made to clean the HVPs again.

> **Recommendation 14**
> National standards for the return of New Dimension assets post incident need to be set by the New Dimension team and agreed by all FRSs.

14/12/2005
18:36:45 Key HOSE CLEANING REQUIRED FOR ALL HVP - CREW REQUIRED AT 0900 AND FURTHER REQUIRED AT 1100 - RV POINT AT THE BASE RESERVOIR - TOP RESERVOIR ON BREAKSPEAR WAY - 189 WILL BEING CALLING BACK TO CONFIRM IF HFRS NEED TO ORGANISE

15/12/2005
20:22:28 Informative   AS PREVIOUS - FOLLOWING MEETING WITH ALL EXTERNAL AGENCIES ON SITE- AN AGREEMENT WAS REACHED ON LIMITED REMOVAL OF RUN OFF FROM INCIDENT - FURTHER MEETING TO TAKE PLACE 2100HRS TO DISCUSS FURTHER ACTION TO BE TAKEN BY SITE OWNERS FOR REMOVAL OF ALL CONTAMINATED RUN OFF - TM OSCAR

16/12/2005
20:03:11 Informative FROM F1 AT SA -FORWARD CONTROL POINT NOW DISBANDED - OSCAR CONTROL RELOCATED TO TANKER FILLING POINT IN MAIN DEPOT YARD

17/12/2005
11:52:46 Key WEST DRAYTON CONTACTED REF AIRCRAFT - THIS IS KNOWN BY WEST DRAYTON AND PERMISSION HAS BEEN GIVEN TO FLY OVER SITE FOR AERIAL SURVEY BETWEEN THE TIMES OF 1130 AND 1230 THE SAFE HEIGHT GIVEN IS 15000 M

17/12/2005
12:41:52 Informative FIRE IN BUND TEN INCH FUEL LINE EXTINGUISHED USING FOAM. FOAM AND JETS LEFT IN SITU BUT NOT WORKING. MONITORING OF SITUATION. TM DELTA

Hertfordshire Fire and Rescue Service | Working to Protect. Acting to Save

88

17/12/2005
15:54:30 Informative   FOLLOWING AERIAL SURVEY OF SITE, FOAM BLANKETS BEING APPLIED TO FOUR TANKS IN BUND E. HIGH VOLUME PUMPS REINSTATED TO CONTROL RUN OFF. GAS MONITORING BEING MAINTAINED. TM OSCAR

20/12/2005
04:20:44 Informative   INCREASE IN RUN OFF IN CHERRY TREES LANE HIGH PROPORTION OF FUEL CONTENT EFFORTS BEING MADE TO DAM AND DIVERT ENVIRONMENT AGENCY IN ATTENDANCE BPA EN-ROUTE TM TRANSITIONAL

30/12/2005
23:48:14 Informative   MAINTAINING AIR READINGS ON A HALF HOUR BASIS - MAINTAINING FOAM BLANKET ON TANK 901 - AT 16.00 TOMORROW CREWS WILL LEAVE SITE AND PERIODIC INSPECTIONS FROM HEMEL AND ST ALBANS WILL COMMENCE.

Figure 30
Number of HFRS appliances per day that attended the incident

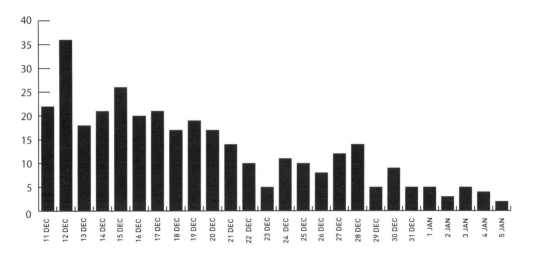

6.10 Environmental protection

6.10.1 The issues of environmental protection are well understood by all FRSs. They are considered during the planning, firefighting and recovery phases of any incident. The size of the Buncefield fire increased the magnitude of potential pollution beyond that which had been previously expected for at this site. This issue was continually discussed at all levels of command and where necessary mitigation measures were put in place. This was often carried out by individual crews carrying out small tasks, such as positioning sandbags to divert or stop the flow of liquids. It is estimated that nearly 15 million litres of water was recycled and reapplied to the fire. An additional 10 million litres of water was moved around the site to ensure containment.

6.10.2 Many of the environmental protection issues also had a direct relationship to safety issues. Plume monitoring and sampling and the subsequent advice received from the health authorities determined the level of respiratory protection worn at this incident.

12/12/2005
04:12:28 Key CHEMET INFORMATION REQUESTED REGARDING SMOKE PLUME TRAVEL AND LIKELY FALL OUT AREA ONCE WATER IN APPLIED TO FIRE

Examples of damage to bund walls

6.10.3 The main area of concern for HFRS was potential fluid pollution of the land that could lead to pollution of water courses. The bunds were monitored to ensure that no overtopping occurred though there is one recorded incident of overtopping. During the main firefighting phase bunds were closely monitored for leaks. Considerable efforts were made throughout the incident to contain all fluids and where this was not successful swift action was taken to limit spread.

> "Further conversation took place between the New Dimension HVP Command Support Officer and the EA representative regarding water supplies. A proposal submitted to the EA and then via the EA to Silver Command was that 7000lpm could be pumped back from the interceptor tank into the holding tank using existing hose and HVPs already in situ. This was proposed as a worst case scenario as no large additional water source was available and because an unknown quantity of water was still required to mix with foam to extinguish the fire. After extensive discussion at Silver, it was decided that under no circumstances was this allowed to happen due to the potential long term contamination of the holding tank." (New Dimension HVP debrief report)

6.10.4 As noted previously, one of the earlier discussions between the Incident Commander and the EA was about emptying the pre-fire contents of the effluent plant onto nearby fields. This was not progressed due to concerns raised by the EA over possible contamination.

6.10.5 The firefighting water supplied by the HVPs was repeatedly shut down to reduce the volume of water being applied to the site and enable further planning and containment to take place.

6.10.6 There was recognition by all agencies that it would be difficult to contain all of the fire water run off. Run off was being well contained until bunds began to fail. This failure caused significant additional operational problems. It was not possible to halt this run off which was noticed to the north of the site. Once this had commenced it was recognised

Bund wall retaining fire water run off

Hertfordshire Fire and Rescue Service | Working to Protect. Acting to Save

90

that this would inevitably continue unless the leaks in the bunds could be stopped. All efforts were then made to lessen the environmental and operational impacts.

6.10.7 On Wednesday 13th December there was difficulty in getting assistance from other agencies when a minor run off from site went under the Motorway M1. Although considered, the motorway was not closed. The source of the run off was identified and stopped within an hour of discovery.

6.10.8 On the Sunday afternoon (11/12/2005) the CFO requested additional information on the environmental issues relating to foam. Concern was raised over whether foam would conform to current guidelines. No guarantees could be given for existing foam concentrate stocks being provided from other sources. Reassurance was given that all newly manufactured foam concentrate would conform.

> 11/12/2005
> 07:26:40 **Agency** Environment Agency Informed ENVIRONMENT AGENCY - INC 365351
>
> 11/12/2005
> 13:07:55 **officer note** THAMES WATER SEWAGE CONTACTED RE RUN OFF - SILVER CONTROL [number removed] INFORMED NO FIRE FIGHTING OF CONSEQUENCE AT PRESENT WILL ENDEAVOUR TO INFORM WHEN WE BEGIN - FROM DO DRAKES
>
> 11/12/2005
> 14:19:51 **Key** THAMES WATER SILVER CONTROL INFORMED WE ARE USING WATER TO COOL SURROUNDING TANKS. IT IS CLEAN AND BEING ALLOWED TO RUN TO DRAINS. ENVIRONMENT AGENCY ARE INAT.
>
> 12/12/2005
> 06:03:03 **Informative** AS PREVIOUS INFORMATIVE - ALL HIGH VOLUME PUMPS IN POSITION - HOSE LINES BEING LAID IN PREPARATION FOR FOAM ATTACK - RESERVOIR DRAINED TO RECEIVE POTENTIAL RUN OFF - BA DUMP BEING SET UP - FOAM CONCENTRATE AND EQUIPMENT BEING POSITIONED - TM OSCAR
>
> 12/12/2005
> 10:03:19 **Key** THAMES WATER AWARE WE HAVE STARTED USING FOAM
>
> 12/12/2005
> 20:49:03 **Informative** 3 SECTORS IN OPERATION - COOLING OF ALL UNAFFECTED TANKS IN PROGRESS USING 3 GROUND MONITORS AND 2 TITAN MONITORS - WATER FROM BUNDED AREAS BEING REDISTRIBUTED - 9 HIGH VOLUME PUMPS IN RELAY FOR FIRE FIGHTING REMOVING EXCESS WATER FROM TREATMENT COMPLEX TO AVOID CONTAMINATION OF WATER COURSES - FURTHER ASSESSMENT OF WATER SUPPLIES IN PROGRESS - TM OSCAR

13/12/2005
02:44:42 Informative   FURTHER COOLING JETS ESTABLISHED - RUN OFF CONTROL BEING ENHANCED - WATER CONTAINMENT PLAN BEING DEVISED - TM OSCAR

13/12/2005
05:25:34 GOOD PROGRESS COOLING - COMMENCE RUN OFF TO CONTAINED AREA - TMO

13/12/2005
13:36:56 Informative   FIREFIGHTING ACTION COMMENCED OF TWO OF REMAINING THREE TANKS - PATRIOT MONITOR IN USE AND VARIOUS OTHER FOAM EQUIPMENT - WATER SUPPLY PROVIDED BY HVP - WATER RUN OFF BEING MONITORED - TM OSCAR

14/12/2005
14:23:33 Informative   CREWS REDEPLOYED FROM FIREFIGHTING TO DEAL WITH SITE RUN OFF - RUN OFF CONTAINED - ACTION BEING TAKEN TO REDUCE POTENTIAL OF SITE RUN OFF THROUGH DEPLOYMENT OF HIGH VOLUME PUMPS. - ALL MAIN FIRES NOW EXTINGUISHED- MAINTAINING FOAM BLANKET VIA HAND HELD BRANCHES - ASSESSMENT BEING MADE FOR FUTURE FOAM REQUIREMENT TO MAINTAIN FOAM BLANKET. TACTICAL MODE OSCAR

15/12/2005
15:23:37 Informative   AS PREVIOUS INFORMATIVE - PLAN FOR MANAGEMENT OF FIRE WATER RUN OFF BEING IMPLEMENTED IN AGREEMENT WITH ENVIRONMENT AGENCY AND THAMES WATER - TACTICAL MODE OSCAR

15/12/2005
20:22:28 Informative   AS PREVIOUS - FOLLOWING MEETING WITH ALL EXTERNAL AGENCIES ON SITE- AN AGREEMENT WAS REACHED ON LIMITED REMOVAL OF RUN OFF FROM INCIDENT - FURTHER MEETING TO TAKE PLACE 2100HRS TO DISCUSS FURTHER ACTION TO BE TAKEN BY SITE OWNERS FOR REMOVAL OF ALL CONTAMINATED RUN OFF - TM OSCAR

15/12/2005
22:11:29 Informative   FOLLOWING SITE MEETING AT 21.00HRS A TARGET TIME OF 12.00HRS ON FRIDAY 16TH DEC HAS BEEN AGREED FOR COMMENCEMENT OF REMOVAL OF CONTAMINATED RUN OFF FROM INCIDENT-TM OSCAR

17/12/2005
15:54:30 Informative   FOLLOWING AERIAL SURVEY OF SITE, FOAM BLANKETS BEING APPLIED TO FOUR TANKS IN BUND E. HIGH VOLUME PUMPS REINSTATED TO CONTROL RUN OFF. GAS MONITORING BEING MAINTAINED. TM OSCAR

92

Hertfordshire Fire and Rescue Service | Working to Protect. Acting to Save

18/12/2005
22:02:41 Informative   PREVIOUS WATER RUN OFF NOW CONTAINED
USING SANDBAGS - AREA CONTINUALLY BEING MONITORED - TM
OSCAR

20/12/2005
04:20:44 Informative   INCREASE IN RUN OFF IN CHERRY TREES
LANE HIGH PROPORTION OF FUEL CONTENT EFFORTS BEING
MADE TO DAM AND DIVERT ENVIRONMENT AGENCY IN
ATTENDANCE BPA EN-ROUTE TM TRANSITIONAL

7 Appliances, Equipment and Uniform

7.1 Overview

7.1.1 This section considers what appliances and equipment were used, how they performed and what additional equipment would have been useful.

7.1.2 A huge variety of appliances and equipment were deployed to the scene (Figure 31). The vast majority of equipment performed well within expected performance levels with little need to undertake routine maintenance during the incident. Specialist equipment (from the New Dimension programme and industry fire brigades) supplemented that available to HFRS and provided significant additional capability.

Figure 31
List of different appliances used at the fireground

7.1.3 As might be expected on a large and protracted incident, a number of comments were received in relation to personal protective equipment (PPE). The other main area of discussion was in regard to the information technology available to fire personnel at multi-agency commands, HFRS Control and in the HFRS Control Unit with numerous comments on communication and documentary recording.

List of Different Appliances used:
4 wheel drive vehicles
Aerial Ladder Platform
Boat
Bulk foam Lorries
Cars
Control unit
Crane
Double Hose Boxes
Equipment Pods
Fire appliances
Fire Response Units
Foam pods
Foam tenders
Foam tenders with cannon
High Volume Pumps
Hydraulic Platform
Incident Response Unit with Forklift truck
Landrovers
Lighting Units
Personnel carrying Vehicles
Urban Search & Rescue Module 4 with Multi purpose vehicle
Various Lorries carrying foam in containers

7.2 Water

7.2.1 The overall view on water supplies was that the equipment used performed exceptionally well, enabling 53 million litres of water to be delivered to the fireground, 15 million litres re-circulated and 10 million litres pumped around site for environmental protection.

7.3 Pumps

7.3.1 The 2250 lpm pumps on HFRS appliances performed faultlessly with 5 pumps working almost continually at near maximum capacity from Sunday to Wednesday.

Pumps at the Million litre EWS

11/12/2005
23:24 Informative FIVE MAJOR PUMPS IN USE FROM OPEN WATER - TM OSCAR

7.3.2   During the main firefighting phase only eight fire appliance pumps were used for pumping. There are no records of any breakdowns.

7.4   High Volume Pumps (HVPs)

7.4.1   15 HVPs were used to great benefit during the incident (Figure 32). Each can pump 7000 lpm over a distance of 3km.

Fire & Rescue Service	High Volume Pump	Double Hosebox
London	2	2
Royal Berkshire	1	1
Norfolk	1	1
Somerset	1	1
Staffordshire	1	1
Derbyshire	1	1
Greater Manchester	1	0
Northamptonshire	1	1
North Yorkshire	1	0
South Yorkshire	1	0
Fire Service College	4	2

Figure 32
Table of HVPs deployed

Note: In addition, Nottinghamshire FRS, Devon FRS and Cornwall County Fire Brigade provided HVP operators to act as relief crews during the incident.

7.4.2   Taking into account the hose size and pumping capacity differences between conventional fire appliances and HVPs, it is estimated that the use of 15 HVPs equated to 160 fire appliances. Many debrief reports recognise the benefit of the HVPs and several personnel have stated that "we would never have done it without them".

7.4.3   Six HVPs were deployed at the Balancing Tank to supply water for firefighting, including cooling jets and foam production. In addition to the water supply functions, HVPs were deployed at other locations on the fireground as booster pumps, to pump water as part of the water recycling and environmental protection recirculation systems.

Hertfordshire Fire and Rescue Service | Working to Protect. Acting to Save

96

7.4.4   Fifty HVPs have been purchased for the FRS by the DCLG and have been allocated in conjunction with the Chief Fire Officers Association (CFOA) following the results of a socio-economic impact analysis of flooding. The high volume pumps have been provided to the FRS in two phases. The first ten were provided, one per region, in April 2005. The second phase consists of a further forty HVPs which have been rolled out to the FRS between September 2005 and April 2006. It is not surprising that there were a number of comments relating to the unfamiliarity of personnel with the equipment.

7.4.5   At the time of the incident HFRS had just taken delivery of a HVP, but had only just commenced the minimum three month training schedule necessary to enable its deployment. This explains the level of awareness in HFRS of the HVPs capabilities.

7.4.6   This was an extremely valuable operational experience for the 13 FRSs that provided HVP crews. Additionally the Fire Service College released their HVP instructors to assist at the incident. This has ensured that "lessons learned" are being directly fed back into future training courses enabling all FRSs to benefit.

7.4.7   Some HFRS crews were trained to maintain the pumps in operation. This allowed nationally deployed crews to return home. These national crews remained on call and returned when it was time to "make up" the equipment.

7.4.8   The HVPs themselves operated within expected levels and were used until the 28th December 2005. Prior to the main foam attack, the hose layers (associated with the HVPs) completed the task of laying 12 lines of hose over 1.8 km in less than an hour. In total 33 km of HV hose was laid. One additional consideration for national deployment would be a vehicle that carries "ancillary equipment, gate valves, lighting and other spares." (West Midlands regional planner).

7.5   Hose

7.5.1   The main lay flat hose sizes (diameter in mm) used on site were 45, 70, and 150 (Figure 33). The smaller size hose was run out and made up manually by crews. The larger 150mm hose can be run out at up to 40 km per hour and is also made up using a hydraulic recovery system.

Hose diameter (mm)	Individual hose length (m)	Number of lines of hose laid *	Approximate total length of hose used	Equivalent number of 70mm lengths
45	25	2	500m	N/A
70	25	11	4,500m	180
150	50	23	33km	5,280

Figure 33
Approximate total hose used on site

Note: Northgate building fire excluded. * One line of hose may consist of many individual lengths of hose. The longest lines of 70mm hose were approximately 500m in length.

Hose deployment (left) and make up (right)

7.5.2 Each HVP is supplied with 1 km of hose. 10 hose box modules each containing 2 km of hose were used in support of the 15 HVPs giving a total of 35 km of HV hose available.

7.5.3 Each HVP is supplied with two squeeze hose ramps that maintain the cross sectional area but reduce the height to 100mm which vehicles can then drive over. Placing hose ramps on the main water supply of 12 lines of HV hose was impractical as vehicles would have had to drive over a series of 12 100mm humps. No extra wide hose ramps were available to overcome this.

Hose ramps

> **Recommendation 15**
> The New Dimension programme needs to consider the provision and supply of large capacity hose ramps.

7.5.4 To meet the changing demands of managing water for cooling and foam application, hose was regularly shut down, moved and the water restarted. The planning, time and physical effort involved in this ceaseless task should not be underestimated. This task alone physically drained many crews. Determining what was in use and what could be made up or re-used was time-consuming and complex. A number of innovative efforts were made to address this, one of the most notable was when an officer from a supporting FRS used the top of a table to draw and label all the hose lines.

Hertfordshire Fire and Rescue Service | Working to Protect. Acting to Save

98

7.5.5 Crews noted that it was difficult to make up the hose which had been used to deliver foam. Foam had coagulated within the hose. This could have been avoided by cleaning the hose with water prior to it being made up.

7.6 Foam

7.6.1 It is not surprising that there was considerable feedback on the supply and use of foam. This can in part be attributed to the importance of foam in tackling this fire. The majority of comments relate to the logistical issues in locating foam concentrate stocks and delivering the correct foam to the fireground, when and where it was needed.

7.6.2 Concern was raised at Fire Gold on the Sunday about the possible effect of foam on the environment, particularly in relation to PFOS (Perfluorooctane sulphonate). Following consultation with the FEIC reassurance was given that few foam products contained PFOS and that all newly manufactured foam was PFOS free. The large majority of UK FRSs use protein based foam. HFRS were advised that protein based foams did not have PFOS as an ingredient.

7.7 Foam Supplies

7.7.1 The overall expenditure by HFRS on foam for the incident is in excess of £1.4 million. Foam was sourced and supplied from 25 locations in England and in many cases foam was supplied free of charge. New foam was also manufactured specifically for the incident. Despite numerous logistical difficulties, the fireground never ran out of foam (Figure 34).

Figure 34
Total foam supplied

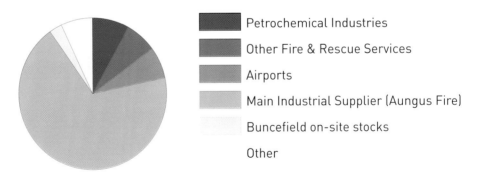

Petrochemical Industries

Other Fire & Rescue Services

Airports

Main Industrial Supplier (Aungus Fire)

Buncefield on-site stocks

Other

Approximate total of foam supplied 876,000 litres.
Approximately 100,000 litres not used.

Supplier	Totals
Petrochemical Industries	71,000
Other Fire & Rescue Services	62,000
Airports	58,000
Main Industrial Supplier (Aungus Fire)	600,000
Buncefield on-site stocks	25,000
Other	60,000

7.7.2 Neighbouring FRSs rose to the challenge of transporting large quantities of foam.

> "The brigade lorry was not capable of moving the quantity of foam required. Permission was sought and given from ODPM to utilise the IRU as a flat bed lorry." Norfolk debrief report

7.7.3 Before agreeing to release foam stocks, a number of supporting FRSs carried out internal risk assessments and consulted with other agencies to ascertain their initial thoughts on the cause of the incident.

7.7.4 A key issue was the supply of foam in appropriately sized containers:

> "Based on feedback received from operational officers and the experience of our own tanker drivers who were helping on the fire ground during the incident, it was clear that the two preferred methods of handling foam were either direct from bulk road tankers or from 1000kg IBCs." Angus Fire report

7.7.5 The national request for foam was coordinated by FRSNCC and was for foam in appropriately sized containers that could be used at an incident of this size. The smallest containers offered were 20 litres ranging up to large foam tenders. The smallest quantity offered was 240 litres and the largest just over 30,000 litres.

7.7.6 The most user-friendly foam that arrived was in either Industrial Bulk Containers (IBC) with a capacity of 1,000 litres or various sized vehicles. One lorry containing IBCs arrived with all of the outlets facing inwards. The forklift truck provided with the New Dimension Incident Response Unit was regularly used moving IBCs around the site.

7.7.7 In ordering foam there was some degree of duplication of effort between industry brigades, Fire Gold support officers, HFRS Control and the nominated HFRS foam officer.

> "Foam inventory control and coordination: our opinion here is based on the fact that there were too many points of contact on foam needs and requirements from the fireground, especially during the early stages of the incident." Angus Fire report

7.7.8 In order to assist HFRS Angus Fire dispatched a company representative to the site.

7.7.9 Calculations and inventories were made within the HFRS Control Unit. Several of the large foam suppliers experienced a delay

Dynamic foam inventory in Control Unit

Hertfordshire Fire and Rescue Service | Working to Protect. Acting to Save

100

between being alerted and receiving confirmed orders. This was probably related to the ongoing calculations of required quantities. At least one of the suppliers operates a use or return policy in emergency situations. Industry sources suggested erring on the side of oversupply during the early stages of an incident, especially given that a number of hours may be required to transport the foam to the fireground.

7.7.10 Several foam suppliers accepted orders by telephone without any formal contract arrangements. They usually made a follow up call to HFRS to confirm that the order was genuine. At least one foam supplier required an emergency supply contract to be signed and faxed back. This took several hours to be completed.

7.7.11 On the evening of Monday 11th, the feedback to major foam suppliers was that sufficient foam was now on site. However, this was quickly revised the next day. Foam continued to be delivered to the fireground until 24th December. Foam suppliers were also involved in the replenishment of foam concentrate reserves kept by other FRSs.

7.8 Distribution systems

7.8.1 Small containers of foam were just one of the obstacles in delivering foam supplies to the fireground. Often, there were no common couplings

Figure 35
Example of decanting route for foam concentrate

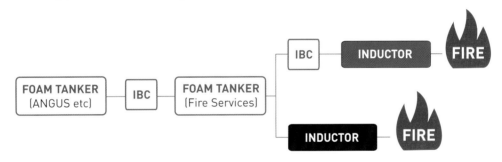

between tankers, FRS pumps and foam systems. This required a great deal of practical firefighting skills and innovation to make up adapters to decant foam from differing vessels (Figure 35).

7.8.2 Five lightweight water cooled pumps each with a capacity of 1,600 lpm were used by crews to decant foam concentrate for use on the fireground. This caused some problems in the pumps themselves due to the different properties of foam concentrate from water. The viscosity of the foam concentrate caused some blockages and some pumps overheated as the foam concentrate did not provide the same cooling effect as normally provided by the water they pump. The pumps were not designed to pump foam concentrate, so the breakdown of these was an acceptable consequence of completing an essential task.

7.8.3 In the main the distribution systems worked well, although:

> "... getting the foam to the fireground was problematic enough but getting foam concentrate from a 25 litre container into a 1,000 litre container would take almost an hour; clearly the small containers were not useful at all." An HFRS officer

"... tankers turned up with little or no means to get the foam from it to another vehicle or branch. Much innovation was needed by fireground personnel to enable foam to be collected from these vehicles and delivered into the tankers that delivered the foam to the branches via inline inductors." An HFRS officer

7.8.4 Crews arriving from out of county had to be redeployed to different sectors to accommodate incompatible equipment. This added to the already complex logistical arrangements in operation.

"Our initial brief was to report to sector 1 to supply foam compound to a foam making pod, but because our foam unit was incompatible with the foam making pod we were sent to sector 3 to assist a high volume foam tender from Total ..." Kent FRS

"Hampshire foam kit also proved very flexible due to dip tube supply system capable of using any supply. Other brigades seemed very restricted to certain types of connections that their equipment required and could not be used at times because of this." Hampshire FRS

> **Recommendation 16**
> Consideration needs to be given to the standardisation of foam couplings or the provision of adaptors between industry and local authority FRSs.

7.9 Delivery systems

7.9.1 Three Angus Titan 4,500l monitors were provided by the site. A large

Site provided Titan 4,5000l monitors on trailer

Hertfordshire Fire and Rescue Service | Working to Protect. Acting to Save

102

range of foam application equipment was brought to the incident by supporting FRSs and industrial brigades (Figure 36).

Figure 36
Table of industry
equipment

Supplier	Resources mobilised
TOTAL - LOR **Humberside**	Specialist personnel EV2 foam tender with 11000 L AFFF F1 foam pod with 11000 L FP70 6 Gun monitor and ancillary equipment Full communication system Gas detection monitors Landrover 4 wheel drive vehicle Equipment pod with 70 lengths of 70mm flame fighter hose 6 long duration BA 4 MEX pourers 1000 gpm oscillating monitor
BP Coryton Refinery	Specialist personnel Williams 6 gun monitor 10,000 AR AFFF
SHELL Stanlow	Equipment and Foam 10,000 L foam
SembCorp Asset **Protection and** **Logistics** Teeside	Specialist personnel Williams patriot II monitor and ancillary equipment Volvo triple agent fire truck with patriot I roof mounted monitor 1500kg dry powder unit 250kg dry powder unit Low loader 4 x 4 MEX bund pourers
Williams Fire and **Hazard Control**	Specialist Personnel

7.9.2 HFRS's foam inductors are designed to operate on a 1-3% solution of foam concentrate. The majority of foam used was a 3% to 6% solution which resulted in variable performance with crews needing to clean them out during use. Hand held foam application improved following the arrival of new pourers.

7.9.3 The majority of specialised foam equipment performed well. As a good example the Warwickshire FRS foam tender and ancillaries performed without fault over almost three days' continuous operation. Elsewhere, regular maintenance checks and some mechanical support were required.

7.10 Foam Concentrate

7.10.1 The range of foams offered seemed to cover anything that had been manufactured in the last 10 years; Alcohol resistant, synthetics, AFFFs and protein foams were all offered in various quantities and quality.

7.10.2 Expansion ratios varied between 1% and 6%. These variations complicated fireground calculations.

7.10.3 The advice received from all experts indicated that given the size of the fire and the amount of foam required, mixing foam types would be inevitable. The view was that this would not cause any significant problems. The decision was taken to allow foam types to be mixed on the fire, but to try to ensure that different foam types remained separate at the point of aspiration. No untoward results were experienced from mixing.

7.10.4 At the beginning of the incident, the type of foam required was not specified. Industry suppliers made their own judgement on the type of foam needed based on the information they gained from those ordering foam and from information provided by the media. A good quality 3% fluoro-protein foam performed best on established fires which had been burning for several days with well developed hot zones in the tank walls.

7.10.5 Some foam blankets deteriorated quicker than others, leading to some questions over the foam grades being used on site.

7.11 Lighting

7.11.1 The fireground was large, so a significant area needed to be floodlit. As the incident took place in winter, this floodlighting was needed for approximately 15 hours every day. The national survey conducted by FRSNCC on 11th December revealed that 31 FRSs had some lighting available. This ranged from a small quantity of halogen lamps to a range of stand alone floodlights and associated generators.

7.11.2 London Fire Brigade (LFB) provided six emergency major lighting units which at the time had not been made fully operationally available within LFB. These operated without fault. Due to a lack of labelling at one stage one of the lighting sets was filled with petrol instead of diesel.

London lighting unit

> **Recommendation 17**
> All equipment should be clearly labelled with fuel type, quantities, restart procedures etc.

7.11.3 Views on the adequacy of the lighting and the timeliness of supply varied. Negative comments noted the lack of ample lighting in the early stages, while positive comments commended the provision once specialist lighting equipment arrived, in particular the quality of lighting equipment and skilled personnel provided by London Fire Brigade.

7.12 Personal Protective Equipment & Respiratory Protective Equipment

7.12.1 HFRS use a contracted out, fully managed service for their PPE. Comments received were generally in respect of fire boots, helmets, the

Hertfordshire Fire and Rescue Service | Working to Protect. Acting to Save

104

changeover of tunics and leggings, and dust masks.

7.12.2 HFRS has been working towards finding a solution to the issue of providing boots to meet the various operational demands. This had been partly resolved by introducing a choice of boots and a customised fitting service. However, problems with fire boots were exacerbated by the large size of the fireground and the distance between the RVPs/ HFRS Control Unit and the fireground. HFRS received only 36 near miss/injury reports, 16 of which referred to boots /blisters.

7.12.3 Crews reported that their helmets caused significant discomfort when worn for long periods. Helmets also created difficulty in hearing commands. Personnel found it virtually impossible to use radios or mobile telephones while wearing a helmet. This led to helmets being removed at inappropriate times within risk areas.

> **Recommendation 18**
> Earpieces for radios should be introduced to enable communication whilst wearing a helmet.

7.12.4 Feedback on the operational performance of tunics, leggings and gloves was virtually all positive.

7.12.5 The only concern raised was the change over of tunics and leggings. Crews were getting through kit much faster than had ever been experienced with some using both issued sets before the first set was returned to their station. By working together, Cosalt: Ballyclare Ltd (who manage the PPE) and HFRS ensured that at all times there was sufficient PPE for all firefighters.

Firefighter at scene |

7.12.6 The issue of respiratory protective equipment (RPE) was addressed mainly by the provision of dust masks. Extensive plume monitoring had taken place and the advice received from health colleagues was that a dust mask would provide sufficient respiratory protection. There were occasional delays with the supply of either initial or replacement dust masks to front line crews. However, once issued crews noted that the non-standard issue FB1 particle mask was very effective.

7.12.7 Very little compressed air breathing apparatus (CABA) was used during this incident. The vast majority of responders were working in a "clean" atmosphere. Air quality on the site only began to degrade to any great extent when the main foam attack commenced and the plume began to settle and swirl around the site.

7.12.8 In reality many Local Authority FRS personnel were not operating within the smoke and therefore did not require CABA. Some CABA kit was worn for comfort at various stages of the incident, mainly by operators of booster pumps on the site. Where out of county FRS personnel were operating within the smoke, their level of exposure was assessed. For example, the level of exposure of those operating the Six Gun was discussed between Essex FRS and HFRS. Essex considered those operating the Six Gun would not be able to do so in CABA. Following this advice it was agreed that these firefighters would use dust masks and crews would rotate every 10 minutes.

7.13 Generators

7.13.1 The only issues raised relating to generators concern the fuel and apply to most of the equipment at the fireground that needed refuelling. First, the equipment was seldom labelled with the type of fuel it required. Consequently there were cases of equipment being refuelled with petrol when diesel was required and vice versa. Secondly, it was noted that HFRS are still using metal jerry cans. Other users, notably the military, have recognised that metal containers for fuel are liable to suffer internal corrosion. The corroded particles enter equipment in the fuel and can cause blockages.

7.14 Appliance Access, Deployment and Parking

7.14.1 There were a significant number of issues relating to appliance access and parking at the fireground. Many of these have been addressed within the fireground and functional sectors section.

> Recommendation 19
> For incidents requiring national deployment a strategic holding area with adequate facilities should be established. Vehicles should be mobilised from there to the RVP close to the incident and then committed to forward deployment.

7.14.2 New Dimension vehicles are currently marked using a national numbering system. They do not have individual FRS/station identity. This means that where they are deployed in large numbers it is difficult to identify them individually and know to whom they belong. This caused problems in matching crews with the keys to specific vehicles.

> Recommendation 20
> New Dimension resources should be identified by FRSs name in addition to the national fleet numbering system.

Hertfordshire Fire and Rescue Service | Working to Protect. Acting to Save

106

7.14.3 There was no system for collecting the vehicle keys of all those parking in the vicinity of the incident, particularly along Breakspear Way. Finding and acquiring vehicle keys was extremely problematic. For example, despite estimates of two hours, it took nearly eight hours to clear the roads of vehicles and equipment to allow the HVPs access for hose laying. Mechanics had to be called to change the ignition key barrel on a fire appliance so that it could be driven clear. Another vehicle was towed away to a vehicle pound and repatriated some days later.

7.14.4 Many issues arose relating to the refuelling of appliances:

- Vehicle fuel cards used more than three times in one day triggered warnings from the card company;

- Vehicle keys and the attached fuel cards were lost;

- Fuel cards were used for the wrong HFRS vehicle and other fire responders vehicles;

- Red diesel was used (records have been kept in case of HM Customs and Excise implications);

- Bearer cards kept for emergency use were not requested from the transport manager.

7.14.5 There were 10 vehicle accidents which resulted in damage by person(s) unknown.

7.15 National equipment

7.15.1 It should be noted that HFRS used virtually the full range of the equipment that has been supplied under the New Dimension program (Figure 37).

Figure 37
New Dimensions equipment used at Buncefield incident

New dimension capability		Module	Total used	Main use at incident
	Water	HVP	15	Water supply.
	Water	Double Hose Box	10	Water supply.
	Urban Search and Rescue	Number 4	2	Multi-purpose vehicle carried on this module used for general site work.
	Prime mover	NA	27	Vehicle used to transport all module types.
	Incident Response Unit	NA	1	Fork lift truck carried used to move equipment and foam stocks on site. Tent system used for R&R.

7.15.2 The familiarity of FRSs with the New Dimension equipment was varied. Among those who had taken delivery and received training on equipment there was reasonable awareness. There were some misunderstandings over the modules and how different modules could be transported together or independently. For example, FRSNCC received information that two modules had been mobilised on a prime mover. However, it is impossible to mount both the modules mentioned on the same prime mover at the same time. At the other end of the spectrum, "some Brigades were also knocking their prime mover off the run when they should have knocked the module off and left the prime mover on the run." (FRSNCC debrief report).

7.16 Other equipment

7.16.1 Further comments were received regarding other equipment that was used or would have been useful at the incident. The vast majority of these related to the lack of fundamental information technology equipment, which many felt impeded the recording and communication of decisions at all commands.

7.16.2 For example, ILO laptops had been supplied to HFRS but not yet configured for use. ILOs operating at multi-agency command had to rely on police IT systems to send and receive information by email or to look up specific information using the internet. In general, a single computer was available to a large number of people to use. This was workable at night, but during the day, availability depended on whether the normal occupant(s) of that office were in attendance. Some minor issues also caused difficulty such as computers timing-out when no one present had knowledge of the appropriate passwords.

7.16.3 ILOs operating at multi-agency silver appreciated the constant display of the police incident logging system. This enabled them to stay up-to-date with developments around the oil depot, which facilitated their liaison role.

7.16.4 At HFRS Control and at the HFRS Control Unit, smart board technology would have aided documentary recording. Smart boards would have enabled information from specific times to be captured, and changes to be recorded progressively. As this was a protracted incident, information updates were required which either confused the original information set out on white-boards or necessitated that information being wiped off and lost. Some officers used digital cameras to record some information before it was wiped, but this did not have the advantage of being accessible to all.

7.16.5 Those working in the HFRS Control Unit felt their recording could also have been improved by the "introduction of laptops and voice activated recording systems".

> **Recommendation 21**
> Modern technology should be used to facilitate briefings, communication and documentary recording.

7.16.6 The HFRS Control Unit crews performed consistently well under pressure. They provided good continuity of support to the Incident and Sector Commanders.

Hertfordshire Fire and Rescue Service | Working to Protect. Acting to Save

108

8 Control Rooms

8.1 Overview

8.1.1 Multiple control rooms were involved in responding to the Buncefield incident. This section will review how they operated, without established national protocols, to provide relief crews, resources and additional information for the incident.

8.2 Main Control Established

8.2.1 HFRS Control worked ceaselessly in the background of this incident. They provided a calm and efficient response to the incident, mobilising appropriate local resources and liaising with both the national control (FRSNCC) and the control rooms of immediately neighbouring FRSs. In addition they responded to calls from members of the public in a reassuring manner. They took appropriate actions in response to the developing circumstances, using procedure as a basis for their decisions.

8.2.2 **Response to 999 calls** - At the time of the incident HFRS Control had a staff of four on duty operating four of the five available positions. There are two additional training positions that can be used when necessary. HFRS initially received 56 999 calls. Due to the volume of calls the 999 call stacking system, which stacks 12 calls, rapidly reached capacity. The automatic rerouting system transferred the calls to other FRSs control rooms. The surrounding FRSs received a further 165 calls. There were no other active calls in progress at this time (Figure 38).

Figure 38
Distribution of 999 calls around Hemel Hempstead

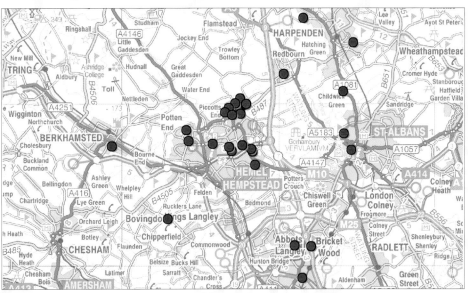

8.2.3 A major incident message was sent at 06:10; such a message triggers a pre-determined attendance and sets in motion the pre-planned actions necessary to deal with major events. Based on the number of 999 calls, the location and the information received from attending crews, the Officer in Charge (OiC) of HFRS Control took a command decision and increased the fire appliance attendance from eight as defined in major incident (MI) procedure to ten and quickly to twelve. The OiC also mobilised and informed officers in accordance with the MI procedure.

8.2.4 Within the team at HFRS Control, one member was designated radio operator with two others handling the 999 calls. Staffing levels were increased to a minimum of six for the first few days of the incident. A number of officers attended to provide additional support and strategic guidance. At the peak there were 12 control staff plus two officers working in HFRS Control.

8.2.5 The OiC also took the decision to reduce the level of attendance to premises that had automatic fire alarms. Any premises that had a pre-set multi-fire appliance attendance were reduced to one fire appliance. All other calls were attended as normal. Between Sunday 11th and Wednesday 14th the HFRS Control Room handled 348 other 999 calls. Amongst these, there were 10 road traffic collisions and 12 house fires.

8.2.6 Incident reliefs and cross county cover- The Buncefield incident opened at 06:02 on Sunday 11th December 2005 and closed on Thursday

Type	Total number of vehicles mobilised to the incident
HFRS Fire or special appliance	591
HFRS Officers	300
Other Fire and Rescue and Industry	183

Figure 39
Vehicles mobilised to the incident

5th January 2006. The main incident log includes over 12,000 lines of data. (Figure 39) shows the number of vehicle mobilisations to the incident. In addition to these, four industry fire brigades attended the incident and were there for the duration of the main foam attack.

8.2.7 In addition to the incident HFRS Control organised all of the cover and standby moves required. Surrounding FRSs provided additional cover within Hertfordshire fire stations. During the "make pumps 25" on Monday 12th some of these appliances were ordered onto the incident.

8.2.8 Due to the distances involved, dynamics of the incident and complexities in communicating, there was difficulty in locating officers and crews that were due to be relieved. This resulted in an increased turn around time at the fireground and multi-agency commands and a knock on effect on the "relief's plan".

> 12/12/05
> 08:30 Informative WILL ADVISE OF TIME FOR RELIEF FOR CREWS- 150 DAY CREW NEEDED TO RELIEVE 150 NIGHT CREW AS CLOSE TO 0900HRS AS POSS

8.2.9 HFRS fire appliances are fitted with an automatic vehicle location system that allows HFRS Control to locate and follow appliances on a computer based mapping system. As crews were rotated off site they often had to leave their own appliance in situ and return on another appliance. The radio call signs did not match the mapping display system which then had the potential to cause confusion. The decision was taken to switch off the visual display in HFRS control. At times this resulted in an unclear situation on HFRS resources at the incident. HFRS Control operators also had to revert to traditional methods to ensure that the nearest appliance was mobilised to non-Buncefield incidents.

Hertfordshire Fire and Rescue Service | Working to Protect. Acting to Save

110

> **Recommendation 22**
> Future upgrades to Command and Control systems should provide the flexibility required to be able to mix and match crews and appliances.

8.2.10 Additional tasks - Numerous tasks were carried out by staff in HFRS Control. The vast majority are the same as those carried out for many other incidents, such as obtaining weather forecasts, chemical data and general resourcing. For example they were heavily involved in sourcing foam, dust masks, bulk petrol and diesel for refuelling appliances, and bottled water for the operational crews.

8.2.11 They dealt with and logged offers of assistance from many sources; many of which proved useful. They even received the offer of helicopter assistance to transport supplies. The local knowledge of HFRS Control personnel was used to good effect. On the rare occasion that local knowledge and contacts were not sufficient further research to locate and acquire the necessary "stocks" was carried out using the internet.

> "Working as a County we are aware of the procedures in place that deal with countywide issues through the County Council and localised issues with the Local Authorities." HFRS Control debrief

8.2.12 As the incident progressed close liaison continued with the police to ensure that foam tankers were escorted in where required.

8.2.13 HFRS Control Unit and HFRS Control crews are experienced; liaison and communication between them is a matter of routine. Some feedback has indicated that an operator's experience would have been valuable at forward control to filter some of the questions asked.

8.2.14 Staff in HFRS Control used the major incident room which is separated from the main control suite by sliding glass partitions. A write on/ wipe off board is used in the major incident room. With no common method of recording there was the potential for information to be missed or erased.

> **Recommendation - repeat of 21**
> Modern technology should be used to facilitate briefings, communication and documentary recording.

8.2.15 After the main firefighting phase there was a great deal of work involved in returning HFRS to normality. Having reactivated the visual mapping element of the automatic vehicle location system the Fleet manager led and worked with HFRS Control to return all vehicles to their home station.

8.3 National Control

8.3.1 The assistance of West Yorkshire Fire and Rescue Authority (WYFRA) was requested at 0750 hrs on Sunday 11th December by the HMFSI Duty Officer. Whilst a Memorandum of Understanding between the First Secretary of State (FSS) and WYFRA had been signed in October 2005 for the establishment of an interim National Co-ordination Centre, the facility was not yet in operation. WYFRA mobilising staff therefore undertook the duties.

8.3.2 WYFRA attempted to carry out the majority of contact with other FRSs by e-mail. This proved unreliable as not all control rooms appear to be alerted to this type of communication and confirmation had to sought by telephone.

> **Recommendation - repeat of 2**
> Systems and protocols to enable national deployment and extended working of fire resources need to be implemented and tested between FRSNCC and others. All potential responders should adhere to accepted protocols and not mobilise until properly ordered to do so.

8.4   Interaction of controls

8.4.1   It is important to distinguish between control centres, communication hubs and decision making centres. The main controls in operation were HFRS Control and FRSNCC. There were also forward controls being operated by HFRS, London Fire Brigade and Essex County Fire Brigade. Each of the supporting FRSs also operated fully or partly via their "home" control.

8.4.2   Decision centres were in operation at multi-agency gold, fire silver and fire bronze commands. The Fire Emergency Information Centre is the gold command for the FRSNCC. For the FRS the multi-agency silver was only a communications hub.

8.4.3   The traditional distinctions between command, control, resourcing and communicating were at times blurred between the five controls, three local commands and one national command. There was a clear understanding of roles but with little direct experience of responding to national incidents, agreed protocols or procedures, personnel carried out actions that they thought appropriate at the time.

8.4.4   At this incident HFRS focussed on local resources and liaised with directly adjacent FRSs and FRSNCC. The FRSNCC requested other FRSs to voluntarily mobilise their own and New Dimension resources to assist with this national incident.

8.4.5   There were liaison difficulties with out of county resources that had been mobilised by FRSNCC. Only one nationally mobilised FRS booked in with HFRS Control. This resulted in HFRS Control being unaware of all the resources operating at the scene. At times this made it difficult to provide information to the home FRS regarding their crews.

8.4.6   The issues of communication are more fully discussed elsewhere. Given the scale and diversity of all participants there were few instances of communications hiccups causing problems and no record of any significant problems. Cross communications issues causing additional or duplicate work relate mainly to the acquisition of resources.

> **Recommendation - repeat of 9**
> A national procedure for the reception, logging and key control of vehicles at incidents involving multiple fire responders should be developed.

Hertfordshire Fire and Rescue Service | Working to Protect. Acting to Save

112

9 Communications

9.1 Overview

9.1.1 This section evaluates the methods and mediums used for communicating during the incident. It also reviews public relations activities and multi-agency liaison.

9.1.2 The issues raised are very similar to those associated with all major incidents and mirror those found in most organisations the world over.

9.1.3 The timely and accurate communication of information is crucial in responding to a major incident. A variety of mediums were used to best meet the communication needs of this incident. The increased requirements for communications between a large number of people and organisations did create some difficulties. However, there were no major failures.

9.1.4 HFRS provided a significant number of press interviews and statements. These gave the media a wealth of information on the developing fire response to the incident. Many personnel felt that more could have been made of this opportunity, even though feedback from the media was very positive.

9.1.5 Liaison was undertaken with a large number of organisations. Existing joint working arrangements established through Hertfordshire Resilience were used to good effect. Although communication with a large number of fire responders was complex, critical information was sent and received.

9.2 Procedures and hardware

9.2.1 **Radio procedures** - Radio procedures were followed during the incident. The comments received recognised that issues were associated with hardware rather than procedures. Key difficulties encountered were:

- Overcrowding on channels;
- Different frequencies preventing all authorities communicating;
- Different procedures operated by visiting specialists.

9.2.2 **Main scheme radio** - A very small number of comments were received in relation to the main scheme radio indicating that it performed within acceptable tolerances. A key difficulty was the volume of traffic being communicated.

9.2.3 **Hand held radios** - Radios were used on the fireground to link different sectors of the operation. Some difficulties in reception were encountered, which may be due to the relatively long distances between the HFRS Control Unit and the fireground. As the incident progressed additional supplies of intrinsically safe radios and charged batteries were sourced, from both FRS and industry, to cope with the changing nature and length of the incident, and the numbers of personnel involved. Not all of the radios sourced reached the incident. During the firefighting phase there was no need for intrinsically safe equipment.

> 13/12/2005
> 19:16 Informative CHARGED FIREGROUND RADIO BATTERIES
> REQUIRED FROM CONTROL

9.2.4 There is a facility on HFRS radios to communicate with other emergency services. This was not utilised at this incident, owing to the limited requirement for the services to interact at the scene.

9.2.5 **Mobile telephones** - Mobile telephones were used as the main form of communications between personnel at the fireground and those operating elsewhere. There was also frequent use of mobile phones to communicate between and among Sector Commanders, the HFRS Control Unit and HFRS Control.

9.2.6 In the region of 2,500 mobile phone calls were made by officers using HFRS mobile phones in the first few days of the incident. Many personnel used the phones on fire appliances or their personal phones.

9.2.7 The mobile phone network provided a valuable, direct and for some issues a very effective form of communication. However, the practice did not conform to standard communication procedures and caused different components of the ICS to be by-passed at times, namely in the recording of information. Phone chargers within ILO packs were used at multi-agency gold and silver. There were insufficient chargers at the incident ground. Additional batteries were sourced and provided but they were new and required charging prior to use. It is worth noting that as the incident progressed the need for intrinsically safe communications increased which necessitated leaving mobile phones outside of the inner cordon.

9.2.8 As personnel changed over they took their phones with them resulting in a continually changing list of phone numbers.

9.2.9 The storage of contact details of specialist personnel on mobile phones proved a critical resource. For example there were no HVP tactical advisors on any "on-call system" at the time of the incident.

> "Communications between HVPs on the incident ground was only successful due to a large number of HVP instructors having each others' telephone numbers in their mobile phones." Derbyshire FRS debrief report

> **Recommendation 23**
> Due to the day and time of this incident, there were no overload problems on the mobile telephone network. **A more robust communications system needs to be developed particularly among senior officers.**

9.2.10 Reliance on mobile phones is not a robust system for dealing with an emergency, but worked in this case.

Hertfordshire Fire and Rescue Service | Working to Protect. Acting to Save

114

9.3 Communications between crews and Incident Commander

9.3.1   A large number of comments were received relating to communications between those operating at the fireground and the Incident Commander. As with any large operation the cascade principle of information applies. This incident was no different with personnel wishing they had more information and awareness. Maintaining the correct balance between the "need to know and nice to know" was an issue. This was particularly so during the most dynamic phases of the incident.

9.3.2   The chain of command was dynamic with the incident being managed as a "matrix organisation". It took time for the newly formed national firefighting organisation to get to know and become familiar with each other. As personnel began to know each other on a personal level the communications between crews, sectors and function improved.

9.3.3   Among some there was a sense that they were not fully aware of who was who, what was happening and why. Many accepted that this was almost inevitable at incidents of this nature and indeed common to many incidents. Communication issues are likely to be behind the perception that the ICS was not as strong as it could have been.

9.3.4   There was some frustration regarding the lack of communication about reasons for two of the six withdrawals. Those commanding the incident ordered withdrawals following on-site risk assessments. Given the volume and breadth of information being received into the Control Unit, there was often very limited time to process and reach a decision. At times only essential communications took place. The critical message to withdraw was passed to those on the fireground who were able to promulgate it to others without direct contact with the Control Unit. Following the safe withdrawals the reasons were communicated to the Sector Commanders.

9.3.5   Congestion on the radio systems and poor reception meant that relays of information were sometimes required. The most guaranteed method was for Sector Commanders to drive back to the Control Unit. They had to do this personally as vehicle insurance does not permit other HFRS staff to drive officers' cars. This caused additional and unnecessary handovers to deputy sector commanders.

9.3.6   Although firefighting helmet markings are very similar between FRSs and industry they do not always convey the same information about the wearer. Helmet markings should be a simple form of visual communication that all recognise. This was not the case at this incident.

9.3.7   Many FRSs only use helmet markings. It was difficult to distinguish between ranks particularly when light was poor, for example, leading firefighter and station officer. There was no problem with FRSs that also had rank markings on their fire tunics.

9.3.8   The system of wearing surcoats to identify the role of the individual worked well.

9.4   Communications between crews and Command and Control

9.4.1   There were numerous lines of communication into HFRS Command and Control. The main line to and from HFRS Control Unit worked well, as did the less formal lines from multi-agency gold and silver. In the main there were no problems for HFRS crews in this area. Communication with supporting FRSs resources that had been mobilised via HFRS Control remained good throughout the incident.

9.4.2   Essex County FRS and LFB attended with their own control units and maintained good on site and home control communications.

Control units
at the scene

9.4.3   When the national resources were mobilised they were ordered to "book in attendance" at the RVP on the motorway and then proceed to HFRS Control Unit. HFRS Control Unit had insufficient resources to log and keep track of these resources within their unit. This resulted in HFRS Control not being advised of these resources.

> **Recommendation - repeat of 5**
> A national system needs to be established to maintain an accurate record of all fire responders at the scene that will enable a rapid head count if required.

9.4.4   New Dimension resources on site were controlled and communicated with by ND staff who attended on a voluntary basis. An ad hoc forward control for ND was set up in an office building adjacent to HFRS Control Unit. This area was used as a reception, briefing and debriefing area.

9.4.5   Given that FRSNCC were not yet operational it is not surprising that there were gaps in the process. In the early stages each FRS that had supplied resources was kept informed by the individuals in attendance, New Dimension team, FRSNCC or the FEIC. As the incident progressed this role was undertaken by HFRS Control. Initial lack of awareness of national resources on site added to the already high workload as HFRS Control gathered this data. This lack of awareness extended across the range of fire resources at the incident.

Hertfordshire Fire and Rescue Service | Working to Protect. Acting to Save

116

9.4.6 Debrief information indicates that industry fire brigades and other industry resources communicated well, where necessary, with their host organisation.

9.5 Photographic Recording

9.5.1 A vast number of images were captured during the incident. These have produced a visual record of events, illustrating many of the components of the fire response.

9.5.2 Very limited imagery was available to the incident commanders to aid briefing and decision making. Multi-agency commands had access to media footage of the incident, but not from the perspective of the emergency responders operating at the fireground. In the early stages, fire officers working from the Control Unit or ND team had no real-time access to images taken by the two helicopters. They had to rely on messages relayed from the helicopter crews or the fire officer taken on board. Accessing the imagery at a later time or even date proved problematic as exemplified by this informative message:

> 17/12/2005
> 14:11 Informative REQUEST FOR IMAGERY RECORDED BY POLICE HELICOPTER TO BE TAKEN TO SCENE ASAP IN A FORMAT THAT CAN BE VIEWED.

9.5.3 A non-uniformed member of HFRS, who had the equipment and appropriate skills, was ordered on to the incident on Monday 12th to start capturing images. Additionally Essex FRS and the New Dimension team mobilised photographers.

9.5.4 Post-incident there has been heavy reliance on images taken by HFRS firefighters, supporting FRSs and industry attendees. The coverage of these pictures is patchy and often does not pick out the detail that would be useful. Many have no or incorrect recorded time and fail to capture specific learning points.

Untimed snapshots taken by personnel

9.5.5 The imagery supplied by the Metropolitan Police helicopter and Hertfordshire Constabulary (Chiltern Air Support Unit) helicopter proved invaluable.

9.6   Public Relations

9.6.1 Staff from Hertfordshire County Council's press office went to multi-agency gold command at Hertfordshire Constabulary HQ. The team joined press office colleagues to handle the initial surge of interest from national and international media.

9.6.2 Extra County Council staff had to be drafted in to cover the phones at the County Council's press office to deal with the continual demand for updated information, explanation and clarification, from early morning to mid-evening on Sunday 11th December. On Tuesday 12th December, a communications manager from Cambridgeshire Fire and Rescue Service also gave support. During the week ending 16th December , the team took over 850 enquiries from the international, national and local media.

9.6.3 In all, 11 Hertfordshire Constabulary Press and PR officers worked 24 hours a day (on shifts) from Sunday to Wednesday morning. They took over 2000 calls about the incident - phones were answered, on average, in under seven seconds. The police press team was supported on mutual aid by press officers from Hertfordshire County Council, Essex Police, Suffolk Constabulary and Cambridgeshire Constabulary and the Government Office of the East England.

9.6.4 Media enquiries were numerous and varied. For example, enquiries were received from the Telegraph, Guardian, Times, Daily Mail, Independent, Express, Mirror and Sun. They came from as far afield as Spain, the Ukraine, Japan, New Zealand (Radio New Zealand), the US, Canada (The Discovery Channel), Russia (Radio Moscow) and Austria (TV Vienna).

9.6.5 The local and national print media carried the story; front pages carried powerful images of the fire and headlines paying tribute to the firefighters – 'Heroes in Hell' ran the headline in one local paper.

9.6.6 As coverage of the incident developed, enquiries from the media became increasingly specialised and technical. Question & Answer sheets were rapidly put together. These covered issues such as:

- What kind of fuel is in the tanks?
- What is their capacity?
- What is a Hot Zone?
- What is the foam to water ratio?
- What is the firefighting process?
- What is a water curtain?
- What are the bunds made of?

9.6.7 The police media line was constantly updated with transcripts of news conferences and other vital information. The County Council's website, **www.hertsdirect.org**, was continually updated to keep people informed about

Hertfordshire Fire and Rescue Service | Working to Protect. Acting to Save

118

developments in the management of the incident, school closures, health advice, road closures and so on. Dacorum Borough Council's website was also updated on a regular basis, with information on access to areas surrounding Buncefield, advice to residents and links to useful sites.

9.6.8 Despite the overwhelming media interest in the Buncefield incident, the Service was praised by many journalists, for being open and for making officers available for interview during an incredibly busy time.

> 11/12/2005
> 08:05 Key 189 - MEDIA LIAISON REQUIRED AT SCENE

CFO during a press conference.

9.6.9 Principal Officers from HFRS gave a large number of press interviews both from multi-agency gold command and from the fireground. Many of those involved in the fire response feel that the opportunity to enhance the Service's professional image was not seized to its maximum. As an example the main media interviews were held at the Police HQ using "police backgrounds". Many are of the opinion that HFRS backgrounds should have been used. However this may show a lack of understanding in that the Police (and normally Police HQ) take a lead in multi-agency gold command.

9.6.10 Site visits were arranged for members of the press pool, and officers who had been at the forefront of the incident were made available to the press. This was seen as very positive.

9.6.11 Other responding FRSs requested that the press go through Hertfordshire's press office. However, some rang the other FRSs back commenting that they could only reach an answer machine in Hertfordshire.

9.6.12 Numerous calls were received at the HFRS headquarters building. Normally these would be passed to HFRS control or the appropriate department. However, there are no written procedures for this non-operational "telephone switchboard" in the event of a major incident.

9.6.13 Internet access to HFRS web pages is via the Hertfordshire County Council website. There was difficulty in explaining this to callers. The HFRS web pages were not updated during the incident, but key information on the incident was added to the County Council site.

9.6.14 Many fire responders have also commented that the Fire Brigades Union press statements during the incident were not appropriate.

9.6.15 Even though the Service has now left the site media requests are still being handled by the press office. Trade magazines such as Fire Times, Fire Magazine and Fire and Rescue Magazine, are all requesting features, photographs and interviews with the CFO.

9.6.16 The magnificent efforts of HFRS and other responders were recognised locally and nationally. Dacorum Borough Council hosted an event to formally thank the responders. The Prime Minister invited multi-agency responders to attend a reception at Number 10 Downing Street. Of the 150 attendees, 100 were from the fire community. They were hosted by the Prime Minister and his wife, the Deputy Prime Minister and the Minister with responsibility for fire.

9.7 Local community liaison

left to right

Firefighter Phil Brannon, Station Officer Jon Smith, Fire Control Operator Sue Hampton, Prime Minister Tony Blair, DCFO Mark Yates and Firefighter Christopher Trim

Sub Officer Rachael Broom and Senior Fire Control Operator and Firefighter Nicki Harvey talk with Tony Blair.

Dacorum Borough Council formal event to thank the responders on on 22nd February 2006 .

9.7.1 HFRS provided an appropriate level of information and answers to queries arising from the public, principally regarding the foam. These were incorporated into multi-agency public messages coordinated by the police according to Hertfordshire Resilience policy.

> 14/12/2005
> 12:27 Key LOCAL SCHOOLS EXPRESSING CONCERN OVER FOAM BEING BLOWN INTO SCHOOL GROUNDS. ADVICE BEING PUT ONTO HERTS DIRECT. SILVER COMMAND ADVISED.

9.7.2 On the Monday and Tuesday evening public meetings were held in local community venues. These multi-agency forums were supported by HFRS Principal Officers. One of the oil companies sent a representative to the briefing on the Monday. It is felt that the presence of a "fire officer", particularly on the Monday, provided a considerable calming influence. These meetings were held to allay fears, address health and safety concerns and generally report on progress.

Hertfordshire Fire and Rescue Service | Working to Protect. Acting to Save

120

> **Recommendation 24**
> Sufficient consideration should be given to possible panel members at public meetings, i.e. consider the likely reaction of the public to certain organisations.

9.8 Service liaison

9.8.1 **Other FRSs** - Many positive comments were received in respect of liaison with other FRSs. These comments came both from Hertfordshire and the other FRSs, mutually praising the way the various crews and officers had operated together during the incident.

Figure 40
Map of other fire responders

9.8.2 Unsurprisingly given the scale of national mobilisation to the incident (Figure 40), there were some issues. Those noted in feedback from other FRSs mainly relate to "discrepancies between the information originally provided by HFRS and the actual situation presented to crews upon arrival at the incident". This quote sums it up:

> "A debrief with the crew has highlighted a number of issues relating to the mobilisation of our resources "out of county" for any length of time. These covered areas such as deployment at scene, welfare support and reliefs. It is my belief that these would have manifested themselves at any incident and as such were not peculiar to Buncefield." Area Commander Operations, GMC

9.8.3 This highlights the need for "brigades to provide as much guidance as possible with regards to resource requirements and duration" (Norfolk debrief report). It also recognises that the onus for dealing with personnel deployed out of county is shared between the home brigade and the host. Some FRSs have noted that in the future they would put in place additional systems at home to support crews deployed out of county.

> **Recommendation - repeat of 11**
> Early consideration needs to be given to the type, quantity and duration of deployment of national resources.

9.8.4 **Other fire responders** - The significant and invaluable contribution of specialist equipment and personnel by industry firefighters has been noted elsewhere in this report. These resources were mobilised to the incident by a range of means. Once at the scene, they operated both as firefighting teams and as consultants to HFRS commanders. Specialists with a huge range and breadth of knowledge of the petrochemical industry also attended. These specialists were able to communicate technical and complex issues in a manner that was clearly understood.

> **Recommendation 25**
> FRSs should establish mutual aid arrangements with industry fire brigades.

9.8.5 Clear agreements on the conditions of attendance were made. This often included the caveat that if an incident occurred at their base then they would have to return.

9.8.6 The successful collaboration of local authority and industry fire responders has been recognised in the majority of comments received on this subject.

9.8.7 Where liaison issues arose, these were the result of changing circumstances, for example requiring equipment to be redeployed at short notice. These caused some inconvenience, but were otherwise inconsequential.

9.8.8 **Multi-agency partners** - HFRS worked effectively with its multi-agency partners during the incident. The vast majority of comments relating to the partners were positive. Most reports note that advice and resources were forthcoming in providing a coordinated response to the incident. Many of the comments relate to the interactions with specific individuals. Some small issues have been raised in respect of particular organisations.

Hertfordshire Fire and Rescue Service | Working to Protect. Acting to Save

122

9.8.9 Hertfordshire Constabulary provided critical operations to support the fire response and in coordinating the multi-agency response. Police forces across the country provided support to fire responders. There is a defined national policy on escorts for oncoming crews, but not for foam concentrate deliveries. Good assistance was provided when requested.

9.8.10 Bedfordshire and Hertfordshire Ambulance Paramedic Service (BHAPS) provided paramedic cover at the fireground for the duration of the incident dealing with minor injuries in situ and conveying only two firefighters to hospital. They scaled down their on site attendance in tandem with the incident scaling down.

9.8.11 Hertfordshire County Council provided significant assistance in resourcing the fire response, particularly through its emergency planning and highways teams. Where the required quantity of a resource could not be provided, workable solutions were devised.

9.8.12 At the incident ground individual representatives of the Environment Agency were found to be helpful and solution focused. All issues relating to possible run off and contamination were discussed and agreed prior to action.

9.8.13 Voluntary organisations provided excellent support in particular through the provision of catering for firefighters at the scene.

9.8.14 Utility companies responded to requests from HFRS to isolate gas and electricity supplies to prevent escalation of the incident. Local water companies were involved in providing and boosting firefighting water supplies and in assisting in the development of environmental protection plans.

9.8.15 Many other individuals and organisations contributed directly or indirectly to the fire response. There is insufficient space to list them all within this report.

Multi agency partners at Gold Command.

10 Welfare

10.1 Overview

10.1.1 This section reviews the welfare arrangements established for the incident and considers what else would have been beneficial.

10.1.2 Welfare arrangements were considered at an early stage and adequate provisions for refreshment were put in place using established links with the voluntary sector. Accommodation for out of county personnel was established at two local hotels. There were some issues in respect of hygiene and informing firefighters' families.

10.1.3 There was broad acknowledgment of the difficulty in providing welfare arrangements for a large number of personnel during a major incident. Many were appreciative of the efforts made. This quote sums it up:

> "Given the range of staff at the scene, the coordination of welfare arrangements was superb and certainly staff from Buckinghamshire Fire & Rescue Service has expressed thanks for the treatment they received." Buckinghamshire and Milton Keynes Fire Authority

10.2 Refreshments

10.2.1 The cost of catering was in excess of £40,000, with a considerable further quantity of catering being provided free by a national supermarket chain. At the incident food and drink was provided on a 24/7 basis from Sunday 11th until Friday 30th December by a range of means and organisations including:

- Hotcans from appliances;
- Supply of food and drinks from Tesco;
- Women's Royal Voluntary Service (WRVS);
- Salvation Army;
- Bedfordshire & Luton FRS welfare unit from Potton;
- Commercial catering van;
- Firefighters eating prior to deployment.

10.2.2 The WRVS were paged at 08:10 on Sunday 11th and informed that refreshments would be required for approximately 100 personnel. The WRVS mobilised locally and were in attendance on the Sunday morning. They quickly commenced work and provided an excellent service throughout their time on site.

10.2.3 During the early stages there were problems ensuring sufficient refreshments reached the crews at the very heart of the incident. Some crews commented that they had operated for 12 hours without what they considered to be proper refreshment on the first day.

10.2.4 Bedfordshire & Luton FRS advised HFRS of their catering capabilities and offered to deploy their welfare unit.

> 11/12/2005
> **12:44 Key** BEDS FRS - WELFARE UNIT MOB TO RV POINT AT GREEN LANE

10.2.5 This welfare unit was situated close to Breakspear Park House. The location was safe and sensible given the marshalling of vehicles and personnel in this area. However, it was over 1km from the fireground which did not improve the provision to some of the most active areas of the incident.

10.2.6 Further supplies of sandwiches and snacks were donated by a national supermarket chain and were delivered to the fireground by an HFRS officer on the Sunday. The WRVS also got their supplies from the same supermarket. There was good multi-agency work with the police ferrying supplies to the most active areas of the incident.

> 12/12/05
> **05:37 Key** WRVS ATTENDING INCIDENT - INITIALLY PROVIDING REFRESHMENTS FOR 60 BUT AWARE THAT REFRESHMENTS ARE REQUIRED IN EXCESS OF 100 FOR THE NEXT 12 HOURS - BURGER VAN CREW ARE RETURNING FOR 0645 - WRVS WILL TRY TO GET TO INCIDENT FOR 0645

10.2.7 Generally the provision of catering improved as the incident progressed. Many crews expressed gratitude whilst at the scene resulting in this comment:

> "Potton's welfare unit was a huge success. We received plenty of positive feedback from lots of people and the crews consistently felt that they were doing an excellent job." Bedfordshire & Luton FRS

10.2.8 There was a hiatus in the catering supply on Thursday evening. At this time and whenever there was a possibility that catering would not be available, every effort was made to inform crews prior to their attendance. This precautionary measure was largely because of the distance from working areas to the catering facility. For example, the following message was relayed from HFRS Control:

> 15/12/2005
> **21:30 Key** ONCOMING RELIEFS TO FEED BEFORE LEAVING STATION AND BRING FOOD WITH THEM

Hertfordshire Fire and Rescue Service | Working to Protect. Acting to Save

126

10.2.9 As the incident continued, the variety and nutritional value of the food available became more of an issue. The weather forecast for the weekend of the 17th/18th December was bleak. HFRS contacted Hertfordshire County Council requesting additional hot catering for the fireground. A commercial catering van was booked to attend from Friday 16th December on a hastily agreed rolling contract. It was very difficult to quantify the requirements for this contract as refreshment was needed for a large number of personnel working relatively short shifts, rather than at regular meal times. Approximately 30 catering companies were contacted before one mobile catering unit agreed to attend.

10.2.10 This catering unit was on scene from 16th to 30th December and even provided a Christmas dinner. The following message was relayed to those working over the Christmas period:

> 25/12/2005
> 13:01 Key CATERING WAGON WILL BE OPEN AND AVAILABLE 24/7

10.2.11 Possibly due to the size of the incident and the mixture of personnel on the site normal cleanliness standards adhered to by firefighters were not maintained. This was noted by some crews, in their words they were
"not proud of the post incident mess – put bin bag in catering packs."

10.3 Toilets

10.3.1 The sanitary requirements of those at the scene were properly addressed following the main firefighting phase of the incident.

10.3.2 In the early days the only toilets available to crews were those in Breakspear Park House, a significant distance from the fireground. This was an issue for all firefighters but obviously more problematical for female firefighters. It also raised a health and safety issue for all personnel as the lack of toilet provision could have discouraged good hydration levels among crews.

10.3.3 There were very limited washing facilities provided. The Bedfordshire & Luton FRS welfare unit is provided with external washing facilities but the majority of crews were unaware of this. The WRVS set up shop in an adjacent office building where there was also toilet and washing facilities. Again awareness of this facility was poor.

10.3.4 Crews who were unable to access these facilities at the main RVP had no access to toilets or washing areas.

> **Recommendation 26**
> The provision of toilet, washing facilities and rest areas must be a component in multi-agency response plans.

10.4 Accommodation & Rest Areas

10.4.1 Arrangements were made for fire crews to be accommodated in two hotels, one adjacent to the RVP with the second approximately 7km from the incident. From Sunday 11th an arrangement was made with the duty hotel managers to reserve rooms. The communications surrounding hotel accommodating varied. FRSNCC was assured that prior to national deployment accommodation would be booked. The HFRS officer nominated to carry out this role made bookings, but was then redeployed to more urgent operational tasks. This resulted in other personnel becoming involved in hotel bookings which led to mixed messages to supporting FRSs.

10.4.2 HFRS had confirmation that hotels had been booked and invoiced. Despite this some crews who went to the hotels had to pay themselves.

10.4.3 Those who did gain access to the hotel facilities found it beneficial and expressed their gratitude.

10.4.4 The hotel on Breakspear Way was also used as a rest area. Its location adjacent to the RVP enabled short breaks to be taken by officers and crews. Some chairs were placed near the burger van during the recovery phase, but these were exposed to the elements. As the incident progressed HFRS deployed its New Dimension Incident Response Unit and the structures intended for "mass decontamination" of members of the public were utilised as make shift crew shelters.

10.5 Shift Durations and Repeats

"It has been acknowledged that this incident was unique and crews were required to work a little longer than would be expected back in service, but the circumstances were such that you wouldn't have missed it for the world. The morale and enthusiasm demonstrated by the crews was a credit to them and they were excellent ambassadors for SF&RS" Somerset debrief report

10.5.1 On Sunday at the multi-agency gold meeting at 12:00 the multi-agency gold commander requested all agencies to ensure a timely turnover of staff at gold command.

10.5.2 At the time of the incident, HFRS had all five of its operational Principal Officers available. This enabled them to ensure that at least one was available at all times. They staffed multi-agency gold, multi-agency silver and fire silver commands. Offers were made from other FRS to provide command level support. This was accepted and an officer from Cambridge FRS attended the HFRS HQ building.

> **Recommendation 27**
> Consideration should be given to a national system of incident command support teams that could be deployed during a catastrophic or protracted incident.

10.5.3 It was recognised that this would be a protracted incident requiring the continued deployment of HFRS and other personnel over several days and, to a more limited extent, weeks. It was also recognised that those involved were working under some degree of pressure for more sustained periods than they

Hertfordshire Fire and Rescue Service | Working to Protect. Acting to Save

128

would generally experience over the course of a standard shift.

10.5.4 A shift system specifically for the incident was therefore developed and implemented on Monday 12th with:

- Principal officers working 8 hour shifts;
- Flexible duty officers working 6 hour shifts;
- Appliance crews working 4 hour shifts.

10.5.5 This took into account two main factors: level of physical activity being undertaken and the availability of resources. Fortunately, the larger number of crews than officers meant those undertaking the most physical operations at the "sharp end" were put on shorter shifts than those undertaking the physically less strenuous work in command positions.

10.5.6 This system did ensure that resources were available where they were needed. Comments relating to shift patterns are spread across the ranks, roles and organisations involved in responding to the incident.

10.5.7 Some HFRS crews felt they spent a longer time at the fireground than they would normally. This message from Control suggests that despite the specific shift pattern, it took some time for reliefs to arrive, be briefed and for crews to be released.

> **13/12/2005**
> **15:36 Key** CONTROL UNIT REMINDED TO RELEASE AND ENSURE THAT RELIEVED CREWS ARE DISPATCHED FROM FIREGROUND ASAP FOLLOWING ARRIVAL OF FRESH PERSONNEL

10.5.8 There was some difficulty in coordinating officers' repeat attendance at Buncefield and deployment to other incidents. Several recall being re-deployed to Buncefield shortly after being relieved at the incident or being deployed to another incident.

10.5.9 There were problems in relieving officers at the incident and there was a considerable time between a relief arriving and the original officer booking off duty. Many fire responders were reluctant to leave the fireground, which was unhelpful. The number of officers to cover all the duties was relatively tight. Delays in going off duty impacted on fresh resources being available for deployment later that day or the next day.

10.5.10 Personnel from supporting FRS were deployed for relatively long periods. Arrangements for relieving these crews varied. In some cases, reliefs were organised by the home FRS, others, particularly the HVP sector, by the national New Dimension team. There was a degree of uncertainty, especially at the beginning, on authority and responsibility levels. Some FRS sent personnel with foam supplies and expected them to return within a few hours, but these personnel were soon absorbed in the incident. The notification of national deployment of resources contained insufficient information about what the deployment involved. They were called upon at short notice and required additional information to plan appropriate relief and welfare arrangements.

"It was noted that due to short notice mobilisation, crews had no change of clothing, personal wash gear or medication that may have been required." Somerset debrief report

13/12/2005
14:03 Key FROM DIVISIONAL OFFICER OF WEST MIDS, WE HAVE 2 PERSONNEL FROM WEST MIDS DELIVERING FOAM. TO HIS KNOWLEDGE THEY HAVE BEEN WITH US FOR 30 HOURS. ADVISE HIM ASAP WHETHER THEY ARE DUE TO BE RELEASED (CONSIDERING RELIEFS)-CONTACT [phone number removed]

> **Recommendation - repeat of 2**
> Systems and protocols to enable national deployment and extended working of fire resources need to be implemented and tested between FRSNCC and others. All potential responders should adhere to accepted protocols and not mobilise until properly ordered to do so.

10.5.11 A further consideration for those crews mobilised nationally was the time involved to drive to and from the incident. Every effort was made to rest crews prior to deployment. Operational considerations resulted in some crews arriving in Hertfordshire proceeding immediately to the fireground, while others were able to rest before being deployed.

10.5.12 Specialists and industry brigade crews were among those who operated over particularly long periods at the incident. They operated at the fireground, not just at command points, and returned multiple times after relatively short breaks.

10.6 Hot debriefs

10.6.1 There are no recorded debriefs of fire personnel in the immediate aftermath of the Buncefield incident. In fire terms, the incident was dealt with successfully and there were no significant injuries or trauma issues to be addressed at the incident. Hence, the normal impetus for debriefs and contemporaneous note taking were not in existence.

10.6.2 There are two wider issues that arise from the omission of hot debriefing. First, the lack of hot debriefs was a missed opportunity to continuously improve during this protracted incident. A hot debrief following the main foam attack would have revealed the issues raised in this report regarding the incident command system and the lack of inner cordon.

10.6.3 Second, the opportunity to gather contemporaneous data on firefighting activities was lost. This has been an issue for data gathering at a later stage, when memories of the incident have become blurred. It is likely too that the relative importance of specific issues has been re-gauged as a result of numerous informal discussions and the passage of time.

> **Recommendation 28**
> A national system should be developed to enable hot debriefs to take place, issues to be recorded and any urgent issues raised to be resolved.

Hertfordshire Fire and Rescue Service | Working to Protect. Acting to Save

130

10.7 Family

10.7.1 A small number of personnel commented on the provision of informing systems for family members, especially of retained crews. Family members had no official sources of information about the incident or avenues to access information about firefighters who were deployed. Personnel not on duty or not deployed to the incident had no method of gaining up to date information and guidance, except for media coverage.

10.7.2 The incident involved the disruption and extension of normal shift patterns for many personnel. Some ad hoc arrangements were made to accommodate personnel who had caring responsibilities both within HFRS and those deployed out of county. For many those at home took second place to the incident. There was heavy reliance on existing support networks.

10.7.3 On a more positive note, there was some good communication on crew welfare to home FRS, for example the following message:

> 14/12/2005
> 16:55 Key INFORMATION FROM SILVER RE PERSONNEL FROM
> BEDS - BUCKS - HAMPSHIRE. ALL PERSONNEL FIT & WELL.
> WELFARE MATTERS BEING TAKEN CARE OF. INFORMATION PASSED
> TO HOME BRIGADES. TR

> **Recommendation 29**
> Consideration should be given to improving the provision of access to information to families of firefighters and on and off-duty members of staff during major incidents.

10.8 Occupational Health

10.8.1 HFRS Control did not advise the Service's Occupational Health Department in accordance with laid down guidance; however Occupational Health did become aware of the incident at an early stage.

10.9 First Aid/Casualty Handling

10.9.1 Cover was provided by Hertfordshire & Bedfordshire Ambulance and Paramedic Service. Two firefighters were conveyed to hospital and minor injuries treated at scene.

11 Health and Safety

11.1   This section reviews the specific aspects of the fire response that impacted on the health and safety of fire responders and others with specific reference to reported accidents and near miss data.

11.2   Due to the severity of the incident many responders reassessed their individual and personal risk matrix. Previously risks that would have been categorised as high were mentally given a lower ranking. This is not surprising given the working conditions on site and a highly professional approach to the task in hand.

11.3   This incident was attended by over 700 fire or special appliances from 32 FRS and four industry brigades. These were supported by over 300 HFRS officer attendances and numerous multi agency or company personnel on site. There are only 37 accidents recorded during this incident which lasted for 26 days (Figure 41).

Figure 41
Breakdown of
reported injuries

Cause	Effect	No. reported
Ill fitting boots	Back/leg pain. Blistered heels	16
Breathed fumes at incident	Chest irritation. Headache and nausea/cough	13
Stepped into inspection chamber at incident	Skin irritation/back pain	3
Cutting bread	Cut finger	1
Foam splashed on face at incident	Eye irritation	1
Allergic reaction to foam at incident	Skin irritation	1
Stepped on to hose reel tubing	Sprained ankle	1
Unknown - reported by other FRS	Unknown	1

11.4   Two of the above injuries resulted in time off work. One of these was for an HFRS firefighter who booked sick with respiratory problems, this resulted in an 80 day absence; the other was from another FRS. No industry brigades reported any injuries.

11.5   There is evidence that briefings which included health and safety matters were carried out prior to crews being deployed onto the site and strong evidence throughout that the vast majority of personnel were very aware of health and safety. There are numerous good examples of this throughout the incident structure:

- Selection of first three RVPs;

- First attendance commitment of only two crew members for dynamic assessment;

- Decision to search for saveable life only on the site;

- Methodology employed in all building searches;

- Consideration of the implications of a day or night time foam attack;

- The six site withdrawals and risk assessed re-entry;

- Safety boat ordered to Balancing Tank when HVPs being deployed or made up;

- Different relief time for different roles;

- Continual plume monitoring and health advice on appropriate RPE;

- Post fire monitoring of air quality and product temperature;

- Emergency training for the air quality monitoring was provided by LFB to HFRS personnel; this permitted the crews to use the equipment but not to further cascade.

Improvised hazard management around the site

11.6   Considering the broad range of physical activities undertaken at this incident, many of which were new to some crews or completely new activities – such as innovative solutions for decanting foam – the evidence suggests that good safe systems of work were employed.

11.7   The noise from the fire and explosions made communications very difficult. Although the explosions quickly subsided the noise from the fire continued for some days. It is accepted that at times fire helmets were removed by personnel while they were within risk areas.

Exploding fireball in tank 12 early in the incident

> **Recommendation - repeat of 18**
> Earpieces for radios should be introduced to enable communication whilst wearing a helmet.

Hertfordshire Fire and Rescue Service | Working to Protect. Acting to Save

134

11.8 Underfoot conditions were treacherous. Almost all of the drain covers and inspection covers had lifted and moved. There was considerable debris from the explosion, much of which was irregularly shaped with projections and sharp edges. Prior to the foam attack walking around the site was a hazardous occupation in itself. Once the foam attack had commenced and large areas were covered in foam the situation worsened. The hazardous underfoot conditions during the remainder of the incident should not be under estimated. There were numerous hose lines spread over 38km, power lines and numerous items of equipment – all of which had the potential to cause a slip, trip or fall. There were only four reported slips/trips/falls during this incident.

Underfoot conditions on site before foam applied

Underfoot conditions on site after foam applied

11.9 At least 5km of hose was initially run out by hand. The number of lines of hose that were run out, moved and subsequently made up has been impossible to calculate. The manual labour involved in this task alone was massive. Considerable further manual labour was undertaken throughout, particularly when moving foam and operating hand held branches.

Hoselines on site

11.10 There is no evidence that a functional health and safety sector was established. Nor is there is evidence that individuals within sectors were appointed to carry out the sole duties normally associated with a health and safety function. Contrasting this is strong evidence from all Functional and Sector Commanders that the safety and well being of their crews was at the forefront of all decision making.

> **Recommendation 30**
> Personnel with operational experience should be appointed at major incidents in order to provide appropriate health and safety advice to the incident commander.

11.11 It has not been possible to calculate the total number of responders who worked on the fire response, nor to count the numbers who worked within the highest risk areas. HFRS alone had 550 fire appliance moves to this incident, each crewed by a minimum of four firefighters. Taking into account the variety and number of attendees, there is irrefutable evidence that there was a safe outcome to this incident.

11.12 This safe outcome was achieved despite the absence of:

- Sector Commanders having a full picture of all responders in their sector;

- The introduction of a comprehensive system to control and monitor access within the areas of highest risk;

- An accurate head count, by sector, of responders following withdrawals;

- An accurate total head count, by HFRS, of all responders following withdrawals.

> **Recommendation - repeat of 4**
> Structured inner cordon procedures must be implemented and maintained at major incidents.

11.13 Post-incident all fire responders have been sent a questionnaire relating to their physical location during the incident and any after effects. The Health Protection Agency is leading on this. At the time of writing no further information is available.

Hertfordshire Fire and Rescue Service | Working to Protect. Acting to Save

136

12 Preparedness - HFRS plan for Buncefield Depot

12.1 Overview

12.1.1 This section sets out the legislative requirements at the Buncefield Depot and reviews the planning and training undertaken prior to incident.

12.2 Legislative Requirements

12.2.1 The Control of Major Accident Hazard Regulations 1999 (COMAH) implement EC Directive 96/82/EC (known as the Seveso II Directive). Its aim is to prevent and mitigate the effects of major accidents involving dangerous substances, harmful to people or the environment.

12.2.2 The regulations apply at two thresholds, the lower tier and top tier depending upon the quantity of dangerous substances stored. Top tier sites, such as Buncefield, must comply both with the requirements of lower and top tier sites.[1]

12.2.3 Local authorities are responsible for specifying the coordinated response of agencies to an on site emergency with off-site effects. Operators have a duty to actively communicate with the public, emergency services and relevant authorities to enable informed decision making. HFRS were fully consulted in the preparation of the off-site plan and emergency multi-agency response arrangements.

12.3 Plan development

12.3.1 HFRS were developing their updated fire plan in accordance with the guidance document "Part 19 of the Institute of Petroleum model code of safe practice in the petroleum industry".[2] The following sections of the guidance were critical components in the development of HFRS's fire plan. Detailed fire plans were jointly developed for every tank on site (Figure 42) This included both foam application and cooling of surrounding tanks.

12.3.2 25,000 litres of bulk foam was provided by the site along with three Titan 4,500 monitors. This was sufficient for a 60 minute attack on the largest tank. Additionally, a telephone number was provided to order further foam.

12.3.3 HFRS's updated fire plan, although in its very final stages of development, had not been formally signed off at the time of the Buncefield incident. Over the past few years, the Buncefield site operators have been fully involved in the development of the HFRS fire plan. The operators have provided pro-active and constructive support particularly in relation to:

---

[1] Establishments on the lower tier must notify the enforcing authority of certain fundamental details, outlined in Schedule 3 of the regulations.

[2] The Institute of Petroleum. Fire precautions at Petroleum refineries and bulk storage installations.

- Detailed information of tank contents;
- General layout of facilities;
- Provision of firefighting equipment including foam;
- Facilitation of on-site exercises.

Figure 42
Firefighting plan
for Tank 907

FIRE FIGHTING HOSL TANK No 907

COOLING INVOLVED TANK

GROUND MONITORS

2

FOAM ATTACK

TITAN FOAM MONITORS

1

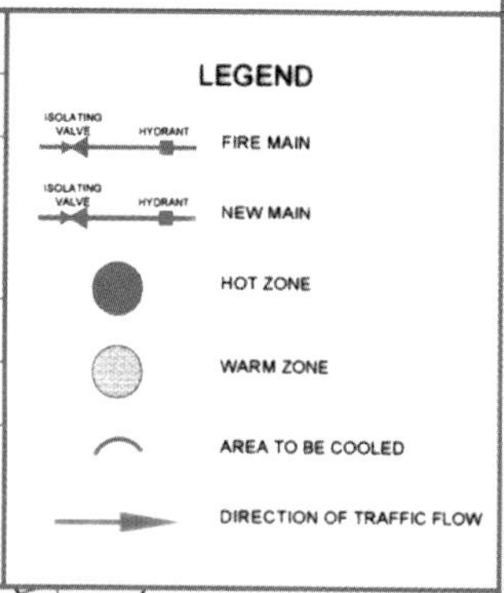

LEGEND

ISOLATING VALVE — HYDRANT — FIRE MAIN

ISOLATING VALVE — HYDRANT — NEW MAIN

HOT ZONE

WARM ZONE

AREA TO BE COOLED

DIRECTION OF TRAFFIC FLOW

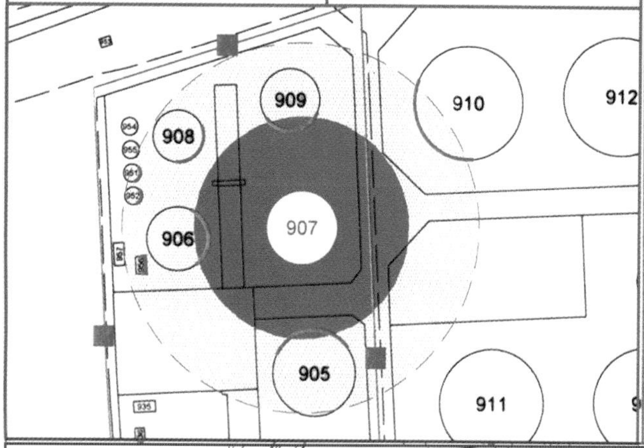

COOLING SURROUNDING TANKS

COMPANY	TANK NO.	MONITORS OR BRANCHES	
HOSL	905	1	2
HOSL	906	1	1
HOSL	908	1	1
HOSL	909	1	1
HOSL	910	1	3
HOSL	951	1	1
HOSL	952	1	1
HOSL	956	1	1

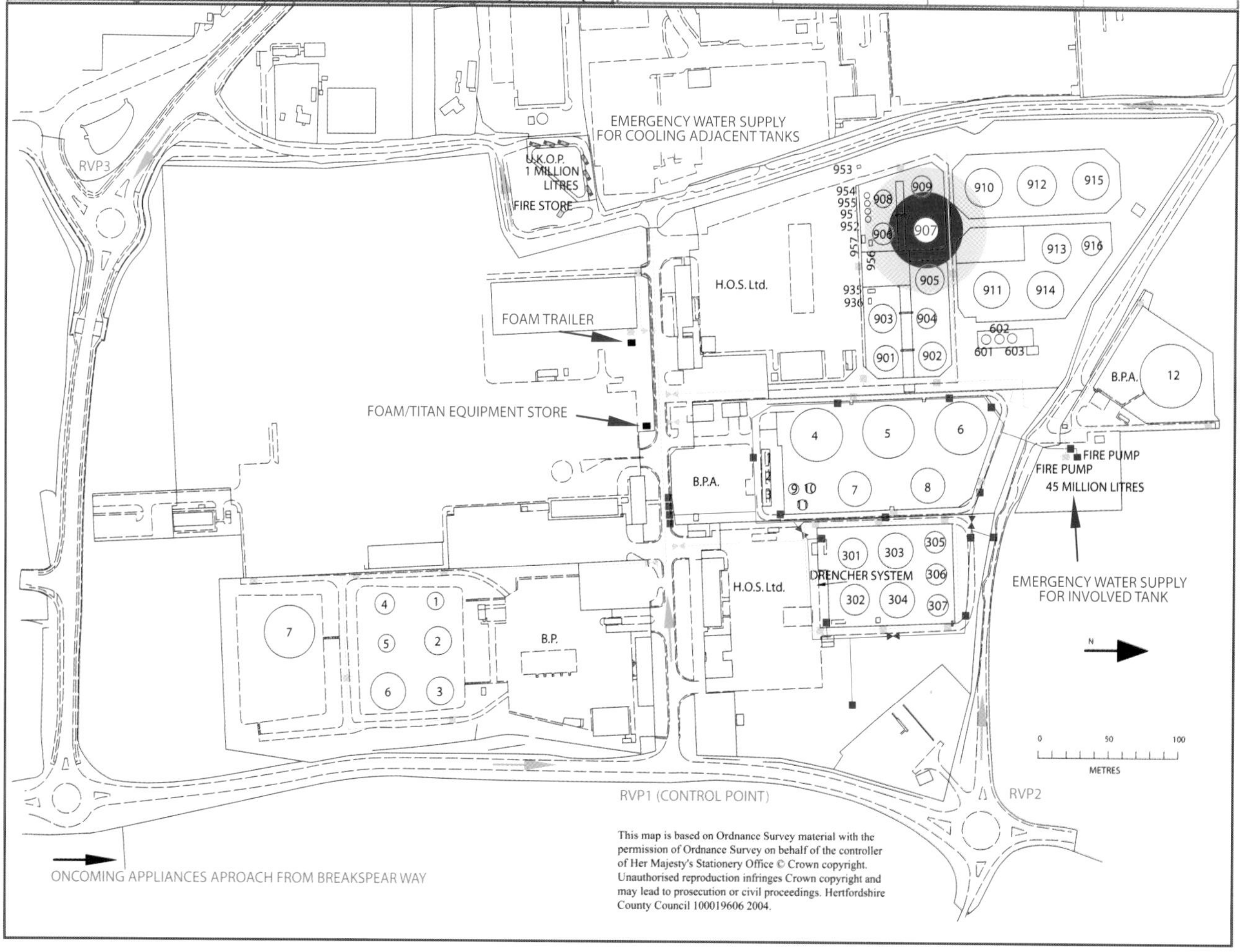

EMERGENCY WATER SUPPLY FOR COOLING ADJACENT TANKS

U.K.O.P. 1 MILLION LITRES

FIRE STORE

FOAM TRAILER

FOAM/TITAN EQUIPMENT STORE

H.O.S. Ltd.

B.P.A.

DRENCHER SYSTEM

H.O.S. Ltd.

B.P.

FIRE PUMP
FIRE PUMP
45 MILLION LITRES

EMERGENCY WATER SUPPLY FOR INVOLVED TANK

B.P.A.

RVP3

RVP1 (CONTROL POINT)

RVP2

ONCOMING APPLIANCES APROACH FROM BREAKSPEAR WAY

0   50   100
METRES

This map is based on Ordnance Survey material with the permission of Ordnance Survey on behalf of the controller of Her Majesty's Stationery Office © Crown copyright. Unauthorised reproduction infringes Crown copyright and may lead to prosecution or civil proceedings. Hertfordshire County Council 100019606 2004.

Hertfordshire Fire and Rescue Service | Working to Protect. Acting to Save

138

12.3.4 The frequency of HFRS's on-site training was designed to allow for maintenance of competency and training with the new equipment. On-site exercises focussed on the practical issues surrounding the application of foam onto specific tanks.

12.3.5 Hertfordshire Resilience conducts one major multi-agency exercise each year, alternating live and simulation exercises. A live exercise was planned for May 2006 based at the Buncefield Oil Storage Depot. The 2005 simulation exercise scenario was a chemical fire and resulting plume.

12.3.6 Following the main firefighting phase, the Buncefield site presented significant additional hazards. These included:

- The potential for foam blanket break down resulting in an unconfined vapour cloud;

- Lack of fixed infrastructure for firefighting;

- Various debris and underfoot hazards as a result of explosion/ fire damage and firefighting activities;

- Potential difficulty in obtaining sufficient resources to extinguish a fire;

- Potential difficulty in containing run off.

Unaffected tanks containing product also remained on the HOSL East and BP sites.

12.3.7 Interim plans were developed to address the ongoing hazards taking into account all the risks present on the site. Significant work had to be undertaken to address containment issues should a further fire occur.

12.4 Buncefield scenarios

12.4.1 The following are examples of incident scenarios for this site suggested during the pre-planning stage. These had not been developed into exercises.

Scenario 1: A supervisor misinterprets a low level tank alarm. Subsequently he gets a gantry low flow alarm and realises he has bottomed out the export tank, so changes over to an alternative tank. The driver gives up waiting to load, leaves an Accuload authorised, and exits the depot.

It is a quiet Sunday morning and the shift supervisor has to go and take a tank sample.

The export pump has had no product circulating and has overheated. When the fresh product reaches the pump, the casing cracks, the leaking product is spilled into the drains and is ignited by the heat from the pump.

The shift supervisor is now a lone worker, on top of Tank 7, with a fire in the pump raft and drains.

Scenario 2: It is shift handover time and the yard is full of tankers. A driver cannot get all grades of product from one filling lane, he manoeuvres past the trucks doubled parked in front of the wash, and the gantry additive pipe work ruptures the tank as he pulls onto another bay to finish loading. The inceptor inlet valve is closed and the resultant spilled product backs up in front of the VSB. The shift supervisor opens the inceptor inlet valve to collect the product in the inceptor chambers.

A tyre fitter is replacing a tyre on a truck, also in front of the VSB, hears the incident, sees the product, and drops the tyre lever. The resultant spark ignites the product which is now draining into the inceptor.

The inceptor outlet valve is partially closed, the chambers are full, and the petrol floats out of the inceptors, around the bund, over the grassed area, and onto Green Lane.

A passing motorist has a dodgy old Ford Escort with DIY fog lamps attached to the underside of the front bumper, and skids on the product, crashes into the complex gates, and an electrical spark ignites the pool of product starting a secondary fire.

The tyres on the truck in front of the VSB are now burning well, the Ford Escort has exploded, blocking the entrance to the whole complex.

Scenario 3: During import from pipeline, tank 7 level gauge sticks and the high level alarm fails. This results in product going over the rim of the tank and into the bund. No fire but potential with fumes blowing across the access road?

Hertfordshire Fire and Rescue Service | Working to Protect. Acting to Save

140

13 National Programmes

The Fire and Rescue Service Resilience Programme

13.1 The fire and rescue service (FRS) is a vital part of the nation's capability for preparing for and responding to major incidents. Together, the Government and the FRS are putting in place practical solutions and investing in new equipment and training, specifically aimed at providing an effective response to catastrophic incidents.

13.2 This includes equipment for dealing with structural collapse, mass decontamination and major flooding – New Dimension. This is part of the Government's response to the events of 11 September 2001, providing an investment of over £200 million for equipping and training the FRS to provide the best possible response to major incidents, including up to £16 million per annum for crewing.

13.3 The need for robust and resilience communications has also been recognised. The Firelink project will deliver a digital radio communications system while FiReControl will deliver a modern, cost effective and resilient linked network of control centres to ensure the efficient and effective deployment of FRS capabilities. Regional Control Centres will be run by local authority owned companies and will be accountable to locally elected members of fire and rescue authorities.

13.4 Firelink is a vital investment in radio communications. It will replace individual fire and rescue services' radio systems with a common wide area radio system for the first time, ensuring interoperability, not just within the FRS, but also with other responders. This radio system will be brought together with new regional control centres (RCCs) built through the FiReControl project to give a resilient communications system.

13.5 All of this work, and that on the wider fire modernisation agenda, is being undertaken in partnership with the Chief Fire Officers' Association (CFOA), the Local Government Association (LGA) and other stakeholders. On the ground, deployment is being supported by FRS personnel, who are ensuring FRSs are ready to receive the equipment and trained in how to use it.

13.6 The ability to respond across borders and in support of other FRSs demonstrates the benefit of a co-ordinated approach to managing the specialist equipment detailed above. Similarly, the National Procurement Strategy, taken forward through FiReBuy Limited, will contribute further to an effective and efficient modern FRS through setting standard and specifications for such specialist equipment.

13.7 By bringing together existing skills with a new generation of equipment and training through New Dimension, a wide-area radio system through Firelink, new resilient regional control centres (FiReControl), and co-ordinated national procurement (Firebuy) the FRS will have an enhanced capability for responding to local, regional and national incidents.

14 National Progress

The following Fire and Rescue Service Circulars - relating to some of the issues discussed in this report - have been issued by the Department for Communities and Local Government. The full circulars can be found at www.dclg.gov.uk under Fire and Resilience.

FSC No: 5-2006   **Date:** 6 February 2006

Title: Guidance regarding Security of Tankers at Fuel Distribution Sites

The Department for Transport (DfT) recognise that there is a need to improve the security of vehicle ignition keys at fuel distribution sites, particularly with regard to leaving keys in the vehicles, which has sometimes been in practice in order to move the vehicles quickly in case of fire. In a time of heightened security this practice needs to be reviewed. The security aspect should now be included in any risk assessments. This circular provides the guidance given to sites by DfT which fire and rescue services should take into account during any assessments of such sites.

FSC No: 29-2006   **Date:** 30 May 2006

Title: Mutual Assistance Arrangements under the Fire and Rescue Services Act 2004

This circular gives guidance to fire and rescue authorities on the types of mutual assistance arrangements available under the Fire and Rescue Services Act 2004. It also outlines the subject areas which such arrangements may cover.

FSC No: 30-2006   **Date:** 2 June 2006

Title: Fire and Rescue Service National Co-ordinaton Centre Guidance Document

The purpose of this circular is to describe the role of the FRSNCC and how it can be contacted, the type of information required from individual fire and rescue services to maintain the effectiveness of the FRSNCC, and the method and frequency for reporting this.

FSC No: 40-2006   **Date:** 12 July 2006

Title: Guidance on the phasing out of PFOS foams for Class B fires

This circular, which has been produced jointly by DCLG and the Environment Agency, provides information and guidance on the phasing out of perfluorooctane sulphonate (PFOS) based foams and seeks local authority fire and rescue services' cooperation in the removal of all of their remaining stocks of PFOS based foams. The circular highlights the voluntary ban on the use of existing stocks of foam being sought by the National Strategic Environmental

Group and provides guidance on disposal and possible alternatives for remaining stocks.

FSC No: 42-2006   Date: 20 July 2006

Title: National Mutual Aid Protocol for Serious Incidents

This circular invites the FRAs to signal their participation in a national mutual aid protocol for serious incidents. The Protocol updates the previous national mutual aid agreement, taking account of the Fire and Rescue Service National Coordination Centre (FRSNCC). The Protocol is necessary to ensure the smooth coordination of specialist (New Dimension) resources hosted by FRAs.

New Dimensions equipment

15 Conclusion, Recommendations and Learning Points

15.1 In summary

15.1.1 The fire at the Buncefield Oil Storage Depot was a catastrophic incident that required a sustained multi-agency response. Firefighters from across the country operated together under the control of Hertfordshire Fire and Rescue Service to search devastated buildings, put the fire out, and commence the process of returning to normality.

15.1.2 The incident resulted in no fatalities and the number of casualties was low. During the response, the safety of responding personnel was maintained with a very low number of reported injuries.

15.1.3 Significant levels of support were received from many quarters throughout the fire response. A great deal of praise has also been rightly bestowed on the fire and other responders, culminating in a reception hosted by the Prime Minister at Number 10 Downing Street.

15.2 Learning

15.2.1 This report has set out a chronological account of the incident from a fire perspective. It has also analysed that response, drawing out points of significance for future planning and responding to major and catastrophic incidents.

15.2.2 The success of the fire response is a credit to all those involved. Key areas of success for the fire response include:

- Safely extinguishing one of the largest fires of this type in peacetime Europe;

- Largest deployment of new national equipment;

- Working in partnership with 31 other FRS and 4 industry brigades;

- The effectiveness of the Hertfordshire Resilience Forum.

15.2.3 With the benefit of hindsight and without the pressure of an unfolding incident, a range of areas for improvement have also been identified. Among these is a need to formalise some procedures and protocols, some are already in development, which will underpin the working practices developed during the incident. Some aspects that require improvement are already adequately identified in Fire Service Manuals, and simply require implementation at incidents. Communications is an area where there will always be room for improvement and equally there is potential to develop smarter ways of working in relation to acquiring resources and providing welfare facilities during an incident.

15.3 Recommendations and observations

15.3.1 The full series of recommendations and observations drawn from this incident are presented below. Observations should be seen as nuggets of information to aid those planning for or dealing with similar incidents; recommendations, in bold, cover areas where a change is needed. The implementation of these will enable the response to major and catastrophic incidents to become even more successful. These have been grouped by disciplines.

The reference to report paragraph is in brackets.

15.3.2 Health and Safety

There is an absolute requirement that all personnel work within agreed command structures and self-redeployment is unacceptable. An inner cordon procedure may have prevented this from happening. [6.8.6] [6.7.12]

Structured inner cordon procedures must be implemented and maintained at major incidents. [5.3.11] [11.12]

A national system needs to be established to maintain an accurate record of all fire responders at the scene that will enable a rapid head count if required. [5.3.11] [9.4.3]

Personnel with operational experience should be appointed at major incidents in order to provide appropriate health and safety advice to the incident commander. [11.10]

15.3.3 Multi-Agency

Hertfordshire Resilience has long established multi-agency major incident working procedures. These have been developed using simulations, exercises and real events. They were of significant benefit to the coordination of the response to this incident. [5.2.9] [9.8.15]

Not all agencies or personnel were aware that the Fire Silver Commander was operating away from the multi-agency silver command, to which a fire liaison officer was deployed. [5.2]

Hertfordshire Resilience should implement a system for taking forward recommendations from multi-agency exercises and incidents. [5.2.9]
Hertfordshire Resilience was well prepared to deal with the media interest during and following a major incident. [9.6.15]

Sufficient consideration should be given to possible panel members at public meetings, i.e. consider the likely reaction of the public to certain organisations. [9.7.2]

15.3.4 Deployment

Systems and protocols to enable national deployment and extended working of fire resources need to be implemented and tested between FRSNCC and others. All potential responders should adhere to accepted protocols and not mobilise until properly ordered to do so.. [5.2.14] [8.3.2] [10.5.10]

Early consideration needs to be given to the type, quantity and duration of deployment of national resources. [6.6.5] [9.8.3]

Consideration should be given to providing advance warning of redeployments for an extended period to all crews but particularly retained units. [5.4.21]

Local and national assessments of the likelihood of further incidents should be undertaken prior to the release of FRS resources under national mutual aid. [6.7.5]

It is essential that all personnel proceed to their designated RVP using defined access routes. [5.3.14]

For incidents requiring national deployment a strategic holding area with adequate facilities should be established. Vehicles should be mobilised from there to the RVP close to the incident and then committed to forward deployment. [7.14.1]

A national procedure for the reception, logging and key control of vehicles at incidents involving multiple fire responders should be developed. [6.4.4] [8.4.6]

Currently there is no standard system for personnel or resources to pass through the outer cordon, except under blue lights. [5.3.18]

Modern technology should be used to facilitate briefings, communication and documentary recording. [7.16.5] [8.2.14]

National standards for the return of New Dimension assets post incident need to be set by the New Dimension team and agreed by all FRSs. [6.9.6]

15.3.5 Incident Command System

All local authority FRSs must work to the current edition of the Fire Service Manual on incident command. Other fire responders should be aware of the incident command system and be able to integrate their working practices in order to ensure a safe system of work. [5.2.20]

Action plans need to be made and kept flexible. The communication of changes needs to be carefully considered. [5.3.6]

Consideration should be given to a national system of incident command support teams that could be deployed during a catastrophic or protracted incident. [10.5.2]

A team of HVP national operational and tactical advisers should be trained and equipped to be deployed anywhere in the U.K.. Consideration should also be given to extending this to all National ND resources [6.6.5]

The key factor in not mobilising specialised urban search and rescue teams was the day and time of the incident and information from people at the premises, which indicated there would be no casualties. In incidents where buildings have received this degree of damage, it would normally be expected that USAR teams would be mobilised to stand by at a strategic holding area or an RVP. However at this incident the correct decision was taken not to mobilise. [6.2]

Consideration should be given to using technology to facilitate briefings, communication and documentary recording. [7.16.5] [8.2.14]

Due to the day and time of this incident, there were no overload problems on the mobile telephone network. **A more robust communications system needs to be developed particularly among senior officers. [9.2.9]**

It is natural that all personnel at whatever level often feel the need to be kept fully informed about the wider picture. There is often insufficient time to inform personnel of issues that are not crucial to their particular sphere of operations. This is always going to be a problem. [9.3.3]

Efficient human resource management systems may have given the incident commander sufficient information to redeploy officers to the same role or sector. [5.2.21]

Operational personnel were able to draw on their skill and knowledge to respond to a dynamic situation of a scale beyond their normal exposure. Experience enabled them to cope efficiently whilst operating under great pressure. [6.5.7]

A national system should be developed to enable hot debriefs to take place, issues to be recorded and any urgent issues raised to be resolved. [10.6.3]

15.3.6 Documentary recording

HFRS should develop and introduce an efficient and effective recording system for all levels of command. It should provide easy access to the decision log and be supported by appropriate technology and training. [5.3.28]

A formalised handover procedure, using a standard system and documentation, would have been of benefit. [5.4.13]

Consideration should be given to using support staff with appropriate skills to aid documentary recording. [5.3.28]

The early deployment of an official photographer would have facilitated the capture of specific images to aid future learning. [9.5.5]

Hertfordshire Fire and Rescue Service | Working to Protect. Acting to Save

148

15.3.7 Resources

Local Resilience forums should develop a single coordinated centre for the acquisition and distribution of all generic resources for all agencies during major incidents. [5.3.23]

Vehicle consumables such as fuel, oil and anti-freeze could have been coordinated through a structured resourcing centre. [7.14.4]

An accurate assessment is required of the areas in which advice is required. Careful selection of advice from the vast range offered during a major incident is crucial. [5.4.25]

When seeking advice be clear what advice is required by when. [5.4.30]

It may have been more appropriate for a single resourcing centre to log all offers of assistance. [8.2.11]

It is beneficial to plan reliefs as far in advance as possible and ensure that all personnel understand and comply with the system established. [10.5.9]

It is accepted firefighting practice to gather sufficient resources to attack and maintain the foam blanket before commencing. There are occasions when it is operationally prudent to tackle small areas at an earlier stage. [6.3.5]

Local FRS Controls had good local intelligence of potential sources of foam (and other resources), which facilitated a national survey. [6.7.3]

Even with industry and international experts assisting, it was difficult to accurately calculate the total amount of foam required. [6.7.2]

A single point of contact for ordering foam should be established. All fire responders should be made aware of this and operate through this point. Industry expertise should be utilised. [7.7.8]

When ordering foam, consideration should be given to the requirements of the whole distribution system including likely rate of use, likely duration of application, decanting and induction systems, and final application method. [7.7.6]

15.3.8 Equipment

All equipment should be clearly labelled with fuel type, quantities, restart procedures etc. [7.11.2]

New Dimension resources should be identified by FRS name in addition to the national fleet numbering system. [7.14.2]

Consideration needs to be given to the standardisation of foam couplings or the provision of adaptors between industry and local authority FRSs. [7.8.4]

Earpieces for radios should be introduced to enable communication whilst wearing a helmet. [7.12.3] [11.7]

FRS vehicles that are owned or leased by the local authority and likely to be used by their own emergency personnel should be covered by corporate insurance arrangements. [9.3.5]

Early contact with the supplier of PPE is essential to ensure the smooth transition from normal business to emergency supply. [7.12.5]

The New Dimension programme needs to consider the provision and supply of large capacity hose ramps. [7.5.3]

Future upgrades to Command and Control systems should provide the flexibility required to be able to mix and match crews and appliances. [8.2.9]

15.3.9 Welfare

It should not be underestimated the multi-agency effort required to provide food and drink to large number of emergency responders over a large geographical area for an extended period of time. [10.2.11]

The provision of toilet, washing facilities and rest areas must be a component in multi-agency response plans. [10.3.4]

Consideration should be given to improving the provision of access to information to families of firefighters and on and off-duty members of staff during major incidents. [10.7.3]

Other

Each fire main pump house and emergency water supply should be positioned and/or constructed such that they cannot be affected by foreseeable incidents. Sufficient hard standing should be provided for the maximum number of mobile pumps that might be expected.

Off site water supplies and their access should be taken into consideration during the pre-planning phase for forseeable incidents at facilities of this type. [6.6.5]

Following incidents, companies and other involved agencies need to rapidly establish protocols to develop and agree a system for handing over responsibility. [6.9.3]

Non-operational switchboards should be provided with written instructions in the event of a major incident. These should note action to be taken when usual channels are too busy to receive transferred calls. [9.6.12]

FRS should establish mutual aid arrangements with industry fire brigades. [9.8.4]

Hertfordshire Fire and Rescue Service | Working to Protect. Acting to Save

150

Glossary

AFFF concentrate

Aqueous film-forming foam. AFFFs are generally based on mixtures of hydrocarbon and fluorinated surface active agents and have the ability to form an aqueous film on the surface of some hydrocarbon fuels.

AFA

Automatic fire alarm

Alcohol resistant foam concentrates

These may be suitable for use on hydrocarbon fuels, and additionally are resistant to breakdown when applied to the surface of water-miscible liquid fuels. Some alcohol resistant foam concentrates may precipitate a polymeric membrane on the surface of water-miscible liquid fires.

Aspiration

The addition or entrainment of air into foam solution.

Assistance message

Message requesting additional assistance to the incident, normally by radio.

Balancing tank

A tank or area that has sufficient volume to permit non-uniform flow of rainwater run off to be collected, stored and pumped to treatment at a more uniform rate. Often used around urban areas to collect seasonal rainfall in order to slow percolation and prevent flooding down stream.

DCLG

Department for Communities and Local Government

BHAPS

Bedfordshire and Hertfordshire Ambulance and Paramedic Service

Branch

Equipment at the termination of a hose line to deliver extinguishing media (See FMB).

Bronze

Operational level that deals with specific issues or tasks at the scene for example a sector commander. This includes the control and deployment of staff and resources.

Bund area

An area surrounding a storage tank which is designated to contain the liquid product in the event of a tank rupture.

CABA

Compressed Air Breathing Apparatus

Call sign

An identifier, normally comprising a name, numbers or letters, by which an appliance or officer is identified when being called by radio.

CCTV

Closed circuit television

COMAH Regulations

The Control of Major Accident Hazards Regulations 1999

COMAH sites	A site to which the COMAH regulations apply.
Command	The authority for an agency to direct the actions of its own resources (both personnel and equipment).
Command point	Point from which Incident Command operates, this may be a car, appliance, specialist unit or part of a building.
Command support	Command support is a role undertaken by one or more staff at an incident. The role typically provides recording, liaison, detailed resource management and information gathering for the Incident Commander. At large incidents Command support may comprise a dedicated team working from a mobile command unit and may include individuals tasked with supporting Sector Commanders.
Concentration	To achieve effective performance, foam concentrates must be mixed with water to the concentration recommended by the manufacturer.
Control	The authority to direct strategic and tactical operations in order to complete an assigned function and includes the ability to direct the activities of other agencies engaged in the completion of that function. The control of an assigned function also carries with it a responsibility for the health and safety of those involved.
EWS	Emergency Water Supplies.
Expansion ratio	The ratio of the total volume of finished foam to the volume of foam solution used to produce it, e.g. 200:1
FEIC	Fire Emergency Information Centre.
Finished foam	The foam as applied to the fire. It will consist of a mixture of foam solution that has been mixed with air. The foam may be a primary aspirated or secondary aspirated.
Fire all out	This is normally a radio message but that preventative fire action will need to continue.
Fire appliance	Standard fire engine with a crew of 4, 5 or 6 firefighters.
Fire surrounded	Normally a radio message indicating that the fire is still burning but is being contained by firefighting action and will not spread further.
Flexible duty officer	Middle or senior operational manager providing operational cover outside of normal office hours generally available on a 78 hour week rota
Foam	The result of mixing foam concentrates, water and air to produce bubbles.

Hertfordshire Fire and Rescue Service | Working to Protect. Acting to Save

152

Foam concentrate	The foam as supplied by the manufacturer in the liquid form; this is sometimes referred to as 'foam compound' or by brand or trade names.
FMB (Foam Branch)	Foam making branch pipe. The equipment by which the foam solution is normally mixed with the air and delivered to the fire as finished foam.
Foam monitor	A larger version of a foam making branch which cannot be hand-held.
Forward Command	Point, near the scene of operations, where the officer delegated responsibility for command in that area is sited.
FRSNCC	Fire and Rescue Service National Coordination Centre. Interim operational arrangements in 2005. Fully operational in 2nd quarter of 2006.
Gold	Strategic level of command involved with the management of the incident.
Head	The height in metres to overcome between the water supply and the point of delivery on to the fire.
HFRS	Hertfordshire Fire & Rescue Service
High expansion foam	Finished foam of expansion ratio greater than 200:1.
Hose ramp	Equipment used to enable vehicles to cross a hose line.
Hot debrief	In this instance a debrief undertaken prior to being deployed to another sector or leaving the incident.
Hot Zone	Area of fire service operations normally close to the fire.
HVP	High Volume Pump. In this instance a pump capable of pumping 7,000 litres of water/min. Provided on two demountable modules. One carrying pump + 1KM of hose. Second carrying 2 km of hose.
IBC	Industrial Bulk Container. A container with 1000 litre capacity.
ICS	Incident Command System. Common system that all FRSs can use for managing incidents
ILO	Interagency Liaison Officer. Officer who has received additional specialist training with other services.
Incident Commander	The officer having overall responsibility for dictating tactics and resource management at the scene.
Induction	The entrainment of foam concentrate into the water system.

Informative	Normally a radio message informing the control room of the progress of an incident.
Inline inductor	An inductor inserted into a hose line in order to induce foam concentrate prior to the water reaching the foam-making branch.
Inner cordon	A secured area which surrounds the immediate site of the incident and provides security for it. Such an area will typically have some formal means of access control.
Key	A message or note relating to the incident as recorded in the Service mobilising system.
Low expansion foam	Finished foam of an expansion ration less than 20:1.
Lpm	Litres per minute
Major Incident	A major incident is any emergency that requires the implementation of special arrangements by one or more of the emergency services.
Make up	Assistance message requesting specific resources, for example 'make pumps 8'.
Make up	Action to clear up and re-stow equipment.
Medium expansion foam	Finished foam of an expansion ration greater than 20:1 but less than or equal to 200:1.
Monitor	A large throughput branch (water or foam making) which is normally mounted on a vehicle, trailer or fixed or portable pedestal.
New Dimension Program	National program to enhance the country's preparedness and resilience by improving the capability of the Fire and Rescue Service to respond to major and catastrophic incidents.
ODPM	Office of the Deputy Prime Minister. Replaced in early 2006 by Department for Communities and Local Government
Protein foam concentrate	Protein foam concentrate contains organic concentrates derived from natural vegetable or animal sources. Hydrolysed products of protein provide exceptionally stable and heat resistant properties to foams although they lack fuel tolerance and have a slow knock-down performance.
Pumps	Shortened term for any firefighting appliance.
PPE	Personal protective equipment

Hertfordshire Fire and Rescue Service | Working to Protect. Acting to Save

154

Rendezvous point (RVP)	Point to which all resources to the scene are directed for logging, briefing and deployment.
RPE	Respiratory Protective Equipment
Run-off	Uncontained liquid, fuel and/or fire water not contained as part of the operation to control the incident.
Sector	The area of responsibility of a Sector Commander.
Sector Commander	An officer tasked with responsibility for tactical and safety management of a clearly identified part of an incident.
Silver	Tactical level of control used for planning and coordination of resources and prioritising of tasks.
Six gun	Large foam monitor
Slop over	When burning liquids, such as heavy fuel oils or crude oils, become extremely hot, any applied water may begin to boil on contact with the fuel, the resulting rapid expansion as it converts to steam may cause the burning fuel to overflow its containment and the fire to spread.
Stop	A radio message informing control that no further assistance is required at the incident
Tactical mode	The mode of operation which the Incident Commander has dictated.
Tactical mode delta (TM Delta)	The operation is being fought with a defensive approach. (Personnel not in danger areas)
Tactical mode oscar (TM Oscar)	The operation is being fought with an offensive approach. (Personnel are in danger areas).
Tactical mode tango (TM Tango)	Combination of offensive and defensive modes in operation at the same time at the same incident (transitional).
Water Curtain	Protective spray to prevent radiant heat igniting other materials or tanks.
Water Treatment	Alternative name for Effluent Plant in North East of site.